A
Harlequin
Romance

OTHER

Harlequin Romances

by ISOBEL CHACE

Many of these titles are available at your local bookseller, or through the Harlequin Reader Service.

For a free catalogue listing all available Harlequin Romances, send your name and address to:

HARLEQUIN READER SERVICE,
M.P.O Box 707, Niagara Falls, N.Y. 14302
Canadian address: Stratford, Ontario, Canada N5A 6W4

or use coupon at back of books.

THE DESERT CASTLE

by

ISOBEL CHACE

HARLEQUIN BOOKS   TORONTO
WINNIPEG

Original hard cover edition published in 1975
by Mills & Boon Limited

SBN 373-01945-9

Harlequin edition published February 1976

Printed in Canada

For MONICA—*again*!

PETRA

' It seems no work of Man's creative hand,
By labor wrought as wavering fancy planned;
But from the rock as if by magic grown,
Eternal, silent, beautiful, alone!
Not virgin-white like that old Doric shrine,
Where erst Athena held her rites divine;
Not saintly-grey, like many a minster fane,
That crowns the hill and consecrates the plane;
But rose-red as if the blush of dawn
That first beheld them were not yet withdrawn;
The hues of youth upon a brow of woe,
Which man deemed old two thousand years ago.
Match me such a marvel save in Eastern clime,
A rose-red city half as old as Time.'

From Dean Burgon's Newdigate Prize Poem ' Petra'

CHAPTER I

The man had no right to be there. Marion Shirley
watched him idly from beneath her eyelashes, wondering why he should have gatecrashed her class. It was
practically the end of term, so it was unlikely that he
had enrolled as a student. Besides, he hadn't shown the
slightest interest in anything she had said all evening.
He had just sat there, making her nerves tingle and dis-
tracting her attention from the lesson in hand. It was
a good thing she knew tonight's subject backwards, she
reflected grimly, or she might have come to a shudder-
ing stop long since under the weight of that lazy stare
with which he had favoured her whenever he had not
been tapping his fingers on the desk in time to some
imaginary tune or, worse still, had gone off into a day-
dream with an inexpressibly bored look written large
on his face.

'So we see,' she said, 'wall paintings are far from
always being true frescoes, which is a very specialised
technique, where the paint is laid on *damp* plaster, so
that it penetrates it and marries into one substance with
it. In many instances Byzantine wall paintings were
executed in glue or a tempera medium, laid upon hard
plaster, in much the same way as they were put on the
gesso background of a panel. Over the centuries, the
plaster sets to a rock-like hardness. The nature of the
plaster varies from district to district, of course, but
when making up your mind what was painted where,
the stylistic evidence is far more important than the
technical.'

She drew a deep breath, glad that the evening was
coming to an end. 'Any questions?' she snapped out.

The man tipped his chair forward and Marion had
a sudden, nervous fear that he was about to ask her
something that she wouldn't know the answer to. It

7

would be just like him to show her up before such a disparate class that she was already finding hard to handle. .

But the question never came.

'Miss Shirley, I asked you if there were any examples of the true fresco in Rome? I'm going there for my holidays later this year.'

Marion turned her attention to the questioner with a burning sense of relief. 'Some of the best examples are there,' she answered. 'Many true frescoes survive in the catacombs and the early churches in Rome.'

She waited to see if there were any more questions, standing quietly beside the tall desk she had been given on which to prop up her notes. She had learned early in her career to let the interest of the class come to her rather than try to impose her own interests in the subject on them. When she had first been asked to teach the History of Art to an evening class at the local adult education centre, she had been amused to discover that the problems of discipline in a class there were no different from the school where she taught. It didn't matter at all that the students had not only chosen to come along, but had paid to do so, there was always someone intent on breaking up the concentration of others, and the same few who couldn't resist challenging her right to control the class. So far she had always won these battles by exhibiting the quiet good manners that had brought her the support of the majority and had swung the prevailing opinion of the class into being on her side, sometimes with a fierce protectiveness that could be equally difficult to control.

If only she had been taller, but even the highest heels couldn't make her more than five feet, two inches. Then she was impossibly pretty, with a fine pair of laughing eyes and an infectious smile that, coupled with a tip-tilted nose and a mobility of expression, was of no help to her in front of the blackboard. Try as she would to discipline herself into presenting a sober mien to the world, the laughter would peep out to undo all her good work and it would be her leading the gust of laughter as it swept through her class. That she was well liked, she knew, but that she was respected as a fully qualified teacher ought to be respected, she doubted. Her students treated her as one of themselves and *that* had caused her nothing but trouble in the teachers' common room where these things mattered almost as much as the academic achievements of the girls concerned.

The smile burst out now. 'That's all, then, for tonight,' she said.

She hadn't meant to, but she found herself seeking out the place where the strange man had been sitting, to see if he were leaving with the rest. But, on the contrary, he was still lolling at his ease on the hard wooden chair that looked as if it might collapse under him at any moment. Her eyes met his, and the thought of him coming to grief there and then brought the laughter to her throat and her lips trembled with the effort of suppressing her amusement.

He stood up and came towards her with the easy movements of a man who was used to walking, and long distances at that. He put a hand on her desk and looked down at her in silence. His eyes, which she had thought were almost black from the other side of the room, were actually a deep navy-blue, she noticed. They were fringed with long, black eyelashes that matched his eyebrows and his short, curling hair. His face was dark as though he lived in the sun, which he probably had, for he had a network of little lines round his eyes which come from looking into the distance under a hot sun. His mouth was straight and disapproving, which made her feel uncomfortable, for the only thing in vision for him to disapprove of was herself.

'There's no need to offer to pay for a single lecture,' she volunteered, unable to bear the silence between them any longer. 'If I don't mark you down as having been present, I don't suppose anyone will notice that

9

you wandered in by mistake—'

'No mistake, Miss Shirley. I came to see what I thought of you.'

What he did think was not much, Marion thought wryly, and wondered why the knowledge hurt. She didn't like him much either, come to that!

'You have the advantage of me, Mr—?'

'Gregory Randall,' he supplied. He said it as though he were expecting it to mean something to her, but she didn't think she had ever heard the name before.

'Well, Mr Randall, class is out as you can see and I'm in a hurry to get home.'

'I shan't keep you, Miss Shirley. All I want to know is if you really know what you're talking about when it comes to frescoes and the like. Do you?'

'Yes,' said Marion.

'Good enough.' The disapproving mouth relaxed into a faint smile. 'That's all, Miss Shirley. You can go home now if you like.'

She was about to tell him that he had no means of preventing her from doing exactly as she liked when she caught sight of the twinkle in the back of his eyes and realised that, in his own way, the man was baiting her, no doubt hoping that she would fly out at him. But why? Was she exaggerating his motives because of the impact he had had on her? He had not, after all, asked any question in front of the class and she had been quite sure that he had been going to.

'Thank you,' she said. She lifted an eyebrow to show her displeasure, but her effect was ruined by the dimple that came and went in her cheek. He was impossible by any standards, she thought, and yet there was something funny about the casual way he dismissed her from her own classroom. 'Did you enjoy the lecture?' she asked him.

'Parts of it. Parts of it I suspected you had mugged up for the occasion, hoping to sound convincing. But you were quite interesting when you were talking about preserving these wall-paintings, and restoring them where necesary in village churches and so on.'

'Byzantine art is my particular interest,' she told him in frozen tones.

The disapproving mouth relaxed still further into an almost genuine smile. 'Oh, quite. Have you done any restoration work yourself?'

'A little. When my father was alive—' She broke off, a little dismayed that she had been about to tell this unlikeable man all about herself when nobody could have said he had offered her the least encouragement to confide anything but the most ordinary courtesies and those as briefly as possible. 'It doesn't matter,' she ended.

He showed no signs of having noticed her discomfiture. 'Know anything about Islmic art?' he asked her.

She shook her head.

'Nothing at all?'

She went on shaking her head. 'That's one of the bits I hope to mug up—if I touch on it at all.'

The disapproving look was back with a vengeance. 'Won't it leave rather a gap in your history of world art if you exclude it?'

It would, but she certainly wasn't going to admit it to him. 'Most of my students are more interested in European art,' she defended herself.

'Then you should call it that,' he retorted. 'European art, not the history of art, which implies a more universal conception than you have so far offered them.'

'One has to be selective—'

'From ignorance?'

'No,' she sighed. Unlikeable? The man was a menace! 'Still, European art has more to offer—'

'May God forgive you, Miss Shirley. I hadn't thought you so insular. What about China? North America? The Indian sub-continent?'

Marion knew herself to be in the wrong, but nothing

11

was going to induce her to admit it. 'I was going to say, if you had allowed me to finish, that European art has more to offer those of us who share the European culture by living here.' She looked up in triumph. He could hardly fault that argument! 'Naturally we want to know more about what is more familiar to us.'

'Then why isn't Turner or Constable your "particular interest"?' he demanded. 'Why Byzantine art, Miss Shirley? Were you brought up with ikons hanging on the walls of your nursery? Or were you more familiar with Mickey Mouse?'

'With ikons,' she said in a small voice.

He put up a hand and smote his forehead. 'Henry Shirley!' he exclaimed. 'Your father, I suppose? Very well, I give you best this time, though I'm pretty sure you hadn't given a thought to such an argument when you planned your lectures.' He turned on his heel, and then turned back again, the navy-blue eyes flickering over her. 'You must miss your father. I'm sorry if I've aroused painful memories for you.'

She was startled and she looked it. 'Did you know my father?' she asked him.

'No, but I knew of him. Like you, he didn't know much about Islamic art and we exchanged some letters on the subject.'

Her smile kicked up the corners of her mouth as the dimple came and went in her cheek. 'Did you learn anything from him?' she asked, veiling her eyes.

'It was he who was seeking information from me,' he answered drily. 'Good night, Miss Shirley.'

'Good night,' she murmured. She watched him go, recalling herself to a sense of urgency with an effort when she remembered that her mother would be waiting for her. She was glad that it wasn't every day that she was called upon to meet a Gregory Randall, and she hoped it would never be her misfortune to meet him again, yet he was quite different from anyone she had ever met before. And a very handsome difference

12

too, she thought with a smile. Now that he had gone, she wondered what it had been about him that had set her nerves on edge. Her mother, she knew, would have pronounced him dishy and would have been disappointed that she hadn't asked him home. It would be a mistake to mention Gregory Randall to her mother, Marion told herself. She would dismiss the whole incident from her mind—and spend the holidays revising the syllabus of her lectures, not because he was right in thinking she dismissed the rest of the world as unimportant, but because it was impossible to understand the movements of European art in a vacuum, and she knew it. Hadn't her father said again and again that the only unforgivable approach to art was the parochial one? And there was this beastly man saying exactly the same thing exposing the major weakness in her series of lectures in one blinding sentence. *May God forgive you, Miss Shirley*! All right, so she shouldn't have loaded the syllabus so heavily with her own particular interests, but it would be a long, long time before she would forgive him for pointing it out to her.

Her mother had ben attending a dressmaking class and was not appreciating having to wait for her daughter.

'Marion, what have you been doing? I couldn't even get a cup of tea!'

'Did Father ever speak to you about a Gregory Randall?' Marion burst out, climbing into her coat.

Her mother's eyes opened wide. 'Of course he did! He writes books.'

Marion's blood ran cold. 'What about?' she breathed.

'I haven't the faintest idea,' Mrs Shirley said comfortably. She set off down the corridor with a frowning look that told Marion she had better hurry after her if they were to walk home together. Her mother gave her that sudden, slanting smile that her daughter had inherited from her. 'Did you like him, darling? He was

13

at your lecture, I presume.'

Too late, Marion remembered that she had decided not to mention him to her mother. 'When he wasn't asleep, he tapped messages to himself on his desk. I hope he doesn't come back next term!'

Mrs Shirley gave her daughter's arm a comforting pat. 'No danger of that, my dear. I remember now quite distinctly that he doesn't live in England, though I can't remember where he does live. You could look him up if you're interested in your father's address book. They wrote to each other quite often. Henry liked him.'

'He didn't like me—'

Mrs Shirley did her best to keep the laughter out of her voice. 'Did you want him to?' she asked.

'Of course not!' The protest was too fiercely uttered to be believable. 'I didn't like him either!'

Marion didn't have to look through her father's papers to find about Gregory Randall. Once she had heard his name she kept on hearing it. It seemed that everyone read his books, and when she went to get herself one out of the library she found she had to put her name down on a waiting list even for one that had been written some four years before.

He wrote historical thrillers. There had been one about the elusive Richard III, which came down rather heavily on the side of the Plantagenet king; another about the gold and diamond mines of Africa in which Cecil Rhodes was not the hero he has often been made out to be; and yet another about the Red Indians of North America in which heroes abounded on both sides. Marion read all three and combed the shelves for more. She found she liked having her history mixed up with a story that was both exciting and believable. She liked his books far better than she had liked the man.

'I wonder what he's writing now?' she had said

14

suddenly to her mother across the breakfast table.

Mrs Shirley had given her daughter an exasperated glance. 'I don't have to ask whom you're talking about,' she had sighed. '*The* Gregory Randall. Darling, I like his books too, but I don't have to brood over them as if he were the only readable writer left in the world. What on earth did he say to you that you can't think of anybody or anything else but Gregory Randall?'

'I just wondered,' Marion had murmured

'Then wonder about something else,' her mother had advised. 'He's writing a book about the Crusades, I believe. He's had it in mind for some time,' she had added as an afterthought.

It was only later that Marion had thought that her mother seemed to know a great deal more about Gregory Randall than she was saying, and *that* was more than mysterious, it was downright uncanny, for her mother was constitutionally incapable of keeping quiet about anything.

She was thinking about this, rather than the rising noise of the girls in her class, when she became aware of one of them standing in front of her.

'You don't mind, do you, Miss Shirley?' the girl was saying.

'Don't mind what?' Marion demanded.

The girl sighed. 'I knew you weren't listening! I'm talking about the holidays—'

Marion's interest was immediately caught. She had been concerned about Lucasta Hartley for some time. Her parents never seemed to be at home and the girl was left to her own devices far too much. When she was eighteen, Marion had no doubt that Mrs Hartley would swoop down on her and launch her in the jet-set life she and her husband shared so happily, but at only seventeen Lucasta was of no interest to either of them.

'Yes, what are you doing for the holidays?'

15

'I'm going to stay with my uncle,' Lucasta replied, looking sulky. 'Nobody else will have me and *he* won't have me either unless I have a responsible adult with me to keep me out of his way. The parents told me to ask you.'

'*Me*?'

'Well,' Lucasta admitted, 'it was my choice to begin with. I thought it wouldn't be too bad with you, but my mother said you weren't old enough—she protects my uncle from anybody who might fall in love with him, at least that's what she calls it. She's jealous of him really. But my uncle said you'd do very nicely and that you could fly out to Amman with me and that he'd pay your fare himself. So will you come?'

'Amman? When? You can't mean it, Lucasta!'

'But I do! You wouldn't have to do anything, Miss Shirley, except make sure that I don't run away with the nearest oil sheik.' She pursed her lips in obvious imitation of her parent. 'My mother intends that I shall make a suitable marriage when the time comes and she will not have me running around with anyone who is not suitable in case the worst happens meanwhile. But she'll brief you about that herself. Though what she thinks can happen to her ewe lamb in the middle of a desert, heaven only knows!'

'Lucasta!'

'Oh, don't pretend, Miss Shirley. I can see you think it as ridiculous as I do, but my uncle is *not to be trusted*. He goes behind her back, and does all sorts of other devious things—'

'*Lucasta!*'

Lucasta grinned. 'He's nice. And *quite* the ladies' man! You'd better do as my mother says, Miss Shirley, and batten down your heart well in advance. If he weren't my uncle, I'd fall for him myself and my mother wouldn't stand an earthly of showing me the door!'

Marion tried not to laugh. 'It's very kind of you to

ask me, Lucasta, but I've already made my plans for these holidays. My mother—'

'I don't think you have to worry about her, Miss Shirley. My family is very efficient when they make up their minds to something and they'll see to everything for you. All my mother asks is that you come home with me today to meet her. It has to be today because she's off to the Bahamas tomorrow and she's only in London for twenty-four hours. You will come, won't you?'

Marion had already made up her mind to say no, but the look in Lucasta's eyes prevented her. The girl was scared, really frightened that Marion might refuse, and she knew, as clearly as if Lucasta had spoken, that if she didn't produce the Art Mistress for tea her life would be unbearable for the next few hours. Well, it wouldn't hurt her to go and see Mrs Hartley for herself. It would be more fitting to explain to her why she couldn't pack up at a moment's notice and take off for somewhere in the Middle East, leaving her mother, so recently widowed, to fend for herself over the next few weeks.

'Yes, all right, Lucasta, I'll come. I'll meet you at the bust stop, shall I?'

Lucasta's glance was distinctly mocking. 'When my mother's at home, she sends the Rolls to collect me. My family travels first class, Miss Shirley, and so shall we, if and when they bother to remember that we exist at all!'

Marion frowned. 'Do you think you ought to talk about your family like that?' she asked gently.

But Lucasta only shrugged, and opened her eyes very wide. 'You should hear what they say about me!' she retorted.

The rest of the day passed in a whirl for Marion. She tried to telephone her mother at lunchtime, but there was no answer. Marion was glad. It meant that her mother was beginning to go out again, and that

17

was a good sign, for Marion knew that if she was missing her father, Mrs Shirley had known desperation at being left alone while still a comparatively young woman. She had needed all her courage to take a hold on her life again without her husband, and not even Marion could guess at the lonely battle she had fought with herself in the long, cold days after Henry Shirley's sudden death.

Lucasta Hartley was standing at the school entrance, scuffing her toes on the gravel drive. She looked younger than her seventeen years and painfully vulnerable. Marion had heard in the staff room that she had been sent out of class during the afternoon and wondered a little wearily why Lucasta had to antagonise everyone whom she felt had been put in authority over her. It was only in the art class, where Marion made a point of leaving the older girls as much as possible to their own devices, that Lucasta shone at all. She couldn't draw for toffee-nuts, but she had a nice sense of colour and a real feel for fashion and the way clothes should be worn, taught to her no doubt from an early age by her mother.

She looked up as Marion approached and scowled at her. 'The Rolls is late,' she blurted out.

'I can't say I'm sorry,' Marion consoled her. 'I'd rather go on the bus anyway.'

The girls brow cleared as if by magic. 'But we really have got a Rolls-Royce, and a Jaguar too!'

Marion managed a smile. She couldn't help thinking Lucasta sounded more like a boastful ten-year-old than very nearly eighteen. 'What kind of car are you going to have?' she asked.

Lucasta gave her a look of pure outrage. 'I'll never have a car!' she declared. 'I'm not going to add to the pollution problem. No cars, no babies, and a vegetarian diet is the best way to live.' She glared overhead at a vapour trail in the sky. 'And no aeroplanes! I think I'll walk anywhere I want to go.'

'You could buy a bicycle,' Marion suggested.

Lucasta's face fell. 'I never learned to ride one,' she mumbled. 'Oh, look! There's the car! I'm afraid you'll have to suffer a chauffeur-driven ride after all.'

The younger girl stepped into the luxurious interior of the Rolls as if it were no more than a baby Fiat. Marion rather envied her her assurance, especially as the chauffeur tucked a rug in over her knees and saluted smartly before getting into his own seat in the front.

'Heavens!' Marion exclaimed under her breath.

Lucasta looked at her earnestly. 'Do you know how many miles to the gallon this car does? My uncle thinks it's as awful as I do. He prefers to walk too!'

But Marion was in no mood to think about anything that might have spoilt the sheer bliss of sweeping through the London traffic almost as if the rush hour didn't exist for that one day of the year.

The house where the Hartleys lived on the rare occasions they were in London was of large, gracious proportions in a quiet cul-de-sac in Kensington.

'Don't let it throw you,' Lucasta advised as they waited for the chauffeur to release them. 'Just keep remembering that it's more than a roof over the Hartley heads, it's a suitable background for the Hartley daughter to be reared in.'

'Very nice too!' Marion approved.

Lucasta looked at her curiously. 'But you're not envious all the same, are you?'

'No, I like my own home too much for that.'

Lucasta looked up at her home, twisting her lips together. 'One day, when I've gone away too, the squatters will find out how often it's empty and move in. What's more, they'll have all my sympathy when they do.'

'I wonder,' Marion said. 'Wouldn't it be better if the homeless had houses of their own?'

'But it isn't fair for some people to have a lot and others nothing at all.'

19

'That's rather an extreme view,' Marion returned. 'Most people have something and, fortunately in my opinion, all people don't want the same things. I don't particularly want to have to look after a whole lot of possessions and have to remember when the Rolls needs servicing, but I expect your parents enjoy having nice things, and why not?'

Lucasta raised a rather sour smile. 'They don't have time to enjoy anything. You'll find out!' She raised the knocker as if to give emphasis to her threat and the door was opened by a timid young woman in a black dress.

'Your mother says you're to take Miss Shirley into the drawing-room, miss,' she breathed in heavily accented English. 'I bring the tea.'

Mrs Hartley remained seated in the corner of a velvet-covered sofa as Marion followed Lucasta into the room. She was much smaller than her daughter and looked considerably younger than her years. She smiled only with care, so as not to disarrange the perfect contours of her face. Marion found herself wondering if she had had her face lifted and, if so, whether it had been recently enough to hurt her when she laughed.

'I see you've come,' Mrs Hartley addressed her. 'I may as well tell you at once that I would prefer my daughter to have had the company of a much older woman, but my brother made himself so disagreeable about having her at all that I felt obliged to give way to him over you.'

'Is he here now?' Lucasta demanded, looking eagerly over her shoulder as if she expected him to walk in at any moment.

'No, he's out. I'm thankful to say that it looks as if he has at last found the ideal girl for him to marry and settle down with. She has no more time for his extraordinary domestic arrangements than I have, and she's all set to persuade him to come back to live in England. It's so inconvenient not to have a relation here to look after Lucasta when my husband and I are away.'

'Where does your brother live now?' Marion asked, horribly aware of the giggle that was building up inside her.

'In Jordan. He's borrowed a ruined castle which leaks like a sieve whenever it rains, which at this time of year is all the time, and employs a couple of Bedouin servants who sound as though they're completely undisciplined.' She shivered fastidiously. 'It's strictly not my scene, but I dare say you're accustomed to a little discomfort, Miss Shirley, and will manage very well. My brother is paying your fare himself, but my husband wishes to ensure that you have adequate pocket money to keep pace with Lucasta. He thought about twenty pounds a week in cash, of course. My brother will meet you at Amman—he's flying out tomorrow, unless Judith changes his mind for him tonight. You will leave on Sunday.'

'I'm not sure—' Marion began.

Mrs Hartley cut her off with a flourish. 'I forgot. Your mother! Didn't she tell you that my brother called on her? He knew your father, or something. Anyway, your mother is going down to his house in Devon and she's going to work for him a few weeks, putting all his papers in order. Apparently she's accustomed to that kind of work. My brother seemed to think she could do with the money.'

Marion stiffened. 'My mother and I manage very well—'

'I'm sure you do, but it would be unkind to upset all her arrangements now, wouldn't it? You leave from Heathrow Airport, Miss Shirley. Lucasta will expect to find you there at the Pan-Am desk shortly after eight o'clock. Oh, and you'll need a visa. You'd better give your passport to Parsons when he runs you home and he can see to it for you. There, I think that's all. I can't think why my husband thinks women are no good at business. Look how quickly we arranged all that!'

21

" We " was an exaggeration, Marion felt. The amusement inside her surfaced as a quick smile. ' Who is your brother, Mrs Hartley? ' she asked in a shaken voice.

'But I thought I told you,' Mrs Hartley reproached her. ' My brother is Gregory Randall. The writer, you know? '

CHAPTER II

' Mother, how could you? '

' Oh dear,' said Mrs Shirley, ' I had a feeling you were going to be angry, but he was so persuasive and it will be lovely to have something to do again. I've felt so old and useless these last few weeks. There's absolutely nothing here I have to do! Gregory wants me to do for him what I used to do for Henry: put all his papers in order and re-type those pages that need it, and put a bit of polish on his house which has been shut up for years— '

' He's getting married.' Marion sniffed. ' And since when has it been Gregory? '

' Since I first saw him. He never knew his own mother and I would rather like to have had a son as well as a daughter, so we agreed to adopt one another as honorary relations. I could hardly call him Mr Randall after that! '

Marion's eyes kindled. ' And what does he call you? Mother? '

' Not that it's any of your business, but I asked him to call me Helen. He always wrote to your father as Henry and it seemed the best solution.'

Marion choked. ' None of my business! ' she exclaimed. ' I like that! You can't foist an honorary brother on to me and then tell me it's none of my business! It isn't—it isn't decent! '

Mrs Shirley looked wise and very knowing. ' What a curious word to choose,' she said mildly. ' And it has absolutely nothing to do with you. It's my relationship, and I'm very pleased with it. If you want to be related to him too, you'll have to make your own arrangement with him— '

' Mother! '

Mrs Shirley laughed, delighted. ' I'd forgotten for the

moment how easy it is to shock the young, or perhaps I thought you older than you really are. I thought you told me he's about to get married? '

Marion nodded. ' To a girl called Judith.'

' Well, is that anything to look gloomy about? '

' Of course not,' Marion denied. But she hadn't liked the sound of Judith and she thought it would be a pity if she succeeded in putting a collar and lead on Gregory Randall and turned him out of his ruined castle in the desert. ' If I'm gloomy about anything, it's the discovery that my mother can be downright *sly*. Father always said you couldn't keep a secret no matter how hard you tried, and now look at you! Meeting strange men behind my back—'

' Henry would have known.' Mrs Shirley saw the hurt in Marion's eyes and smiled at her. ' Don't mind, darling. You're my daughter, not my husband, and you can't wrap me up in the cotton-wool of your protection for the rest of my life. You have your own life to live and I'm the first to be glad whatever you want to do. Won't you be glad that Gregory has made it possible for me to have a niche of my own too? I like that young man so much. He doesn't waste time wondering what the fuss is all about. He's like Henry in that. Henry too, would have *done* something about his friend's widow, and he, too, would have probably have forgotten to say a single word about how sorry he was.'

' And you don't mind my going to Jordan? ' Marion pressed her.

Her mother gave her a surprised smile. ' Why should I? I know you'll be quite all right with Gregory to look after you.' The smile turned into a flash of laughter. ' He'll find some work for you to do too! '

' I am going,' Marion said with dignity, ' to look after Lucasta. *Nobody* has to look after me! '

' No, dear,' her mother teased. ' Perhaps you'll be able to impress Gregory with your twenty-four years more than you do me. *He* didn't know you when you were only two, or when you were only two minutes old.'

It wasn't an argument that Marion was likely to win, so she stuck out her tongue at her mother and went off by herself to start her packing.

Lucasta accepted the five-hour flight as a boring necessity. She reminded Marion to put her watch on a couple of hours in lofty tones and then disappeared behind one of the Sunday papers that the red-clad hostess handed round amongst the passengers. Marion tried to do likewise, but she found her attention wandered, back to the safety checks they had come through to get on the plane at all, and forward to what awaited her on their arrival at Amman when she would come face to face with Gregory Randall once again.

It was hard to tell the nationality of their fellow-passengers. Some of the women in saris were plainly Indian, or Pakistanis on their way to Karachi and, presumably, the men who were with them were their husbands. Of the others, some were plainly too dark to be British, but others confused her by being quite as fair as herself, though possibly more sunburned, yet they spoke Arabic with a fluency that she thought could only mean they were Jordanians.

The five hours went more quickly than she would have believed possible. Lucasta emerged from behind her newspaper to eat the excellent lunch that was served to them and rather grudgingly admitted that travelling by air did save a tremendous amount of time and trouble.

'That's the trouble. It's never one's own pollution one bothers about, but other people's. If I do it, it's quite all right,' she added, the cares of the world resting heavily on her shoulders.

'I expect this flight would have gone ahead without us,' Marion observed. 'I shouldn't feel too badly about it, if I were you.'

'That's what everyone says,' Lucasta retorted, and

went back to her newspaper.

It was half-past five, local time, when they came in to land and the sun was still shining, warming the atmosphere and adding its welcome before disappearing for the night. Lucasta, with an excitement that she couldn't quite hide, gathered up all the hand luggage and pushed Marion out of the plane ahead of her with a surprising efficiency.

'Gregory doesn't like it if one's last off,' she said by way of explanation. 'He hates hanging about for anyone.'

'But we still have to wait for our suitcases to come off,' Marion protested after receiving a particularly sharp jab in the back.

'He'll see to that. All we have to do is get our passports checked and show our visas to the police.'

Marion found she was quite right. Gregory was waiting for them just inside the airport and a handsome tip found a porter who claimed their luggage and argued with the customs official for them just as if it were his own. It was all much easier than Marion had imagined. What was not easy was gathering herself together to greet the man himself once he had emerged from Lucasta's enthusiastic embrace.

'Hullo there, Miss Shirley,' his deep voice claimed her attention. 'Aren't you going to show any pleasure in your arrival like Lucasta here? I think you can do better than that!' He ignored Marion's outstretched hand and swept her up into his arms, kissing her as warmly as he had his niece. '*Ahlan wa sahlan!* Welcome to Jordan!' he laughed at her.

'*Ahlan bekum!* ' Lucasta roared back at him.

Flustered, Marion stood back from them both, her eyes wide with indignation. 'I don't think we're on these kind of terms—' she began angrily.

Gregory Randall put out a hand and pushed her hair back out of her face the better to see her furious expression.

26

'No? Didn't your mother tell you we have adopted one another? We can hardly go on pretending to be strangers after that, can we?'

Very easily, Marion mentally assured him. She raised her chin and glared at him, bitterly aware that her lack of inches made it all the easier for him to dismiss her protest.

'That is between my mother and you,' she said in frozen tones.

'Miss Shirley, he was only being friendly,' Lucasta put in, her eyes as mocking as her uncle's.

'Strangers don't kiss one another,' Marion said primly.

Gregory Randall threw back his head and laughed. 'You're far too pretty to believe any such thing,' he chided her. 'Come on, Marion, forget it! Your objection to my taking liberties has been duly noted and I'll do my best to comply.'

'Then you can start by not calling me Marion!' she flashed back at him, and was immediately sorry that she should have sounded so petty. 'Oh, call me what you like, but I'd be glad if you'd remember that my mother makes her friends and I make mine!'

Gregory gave her cheek a warning tap. 'Your mother would be ashamed of you,' he told her. 'I fancy you're more like your father, Marion Shirley. He was apt to make mountains out of molehills too. I expect you're tired after the flight or you wouldn't be making such a fuss about nothing.' He smiled slowly. 'It's all right, I'm not expecting an apology—'

'I've got nothing to apologise for!' Marion declared, stung. 'It was you who kissed me, if you remember!'

His eyes travelled over her face in open amusement. 'Since you mention it, I don't remember it quite like that,' he told her. He took a long, last look at her mouth and then turned away, obviously dismissing her from his mind. He barked out a command in Arabic to the porter and followed him out of the building to

27

oversee the luggage being put in the back of the car, leaving the two girls to follow in their own time.

'You'll never get the better of Gregory,' Lucasta said in a loud stage whisper. 'Not even Mother gets the last word with him!'

Marion set her mouth in a firm line and forbore to answer. She preferred not to think of that moment of delicious panic when he had lifted her high against him and had kissed her with firm, warm lips that had set her blood on fire and had deprived her of breath. It was outrageous that he should sweep her off her feet —*Sweep her off her feet*? He had done nothing of the kind. Oh, literally, he might have lifted her clear of the floor, but she refused to admit that her heart was only now settling down to a normal rhythm, or that he had had any lasting effect in undermining her hard-won naturalness of manner in his presence. He was flattering himself if he thought his kiss had been anything more than a temporary annoyance to her.

He put the two girls in the back of the car, getting in himself beside the driver. Marion was surprised to see that it was already dark except for a rim of red over the untidy, dusty desert capital of the Hashemite Kingdom. She stared out of the window taking in as much of the scene as possible while the light lasted and they had been moving for some time when she realised that Gregory had turned in his seat and was studying her as hard as she was the scenery.

'Do you—do you live far from here?' she asked him politely.

'Too far to go tonight. I've booked rooms for us at an hotel for the night. It would be a pity to miss your first sight of the desert by driving through it in the dark.'

'Then you really do live in a castle?'

He raised his eyebrows. 'Did you doubt it?'

A note of excitement entered her voice. 'A Crusader castle?'

'No, but I expect you'll see one or two of those too while you're here. Mine is more like a hunting lodge. It's not really a castle at all. It dates back to the eighth century A.D., when the Umayyad Caliphs had their capital in Damascus. They liked the luxury and comfort of city dwelling, but every now and then they remembered they were Bedu straight from Hijaz, Mecca and Medina, and they'd retreat for a while back into the desert, and fly their birds and race their horses. Some of them are famous enough to be a tourist attraction, but mine is a small one, away from the beaten track, and the Jordanian Government allows me to live there for the moment, provided I do what I can to restore it to its former glory. I think you'll like it,' he added with a faint smile.

'If it doesn't rain,' Lucasta put in. 'Mother says it leaks like a sieve. Does it?'

Gregory turned his head. 'I never argue with your mother,' he answered.

'Why not?' Lucasta asked. 'She isn't always right.'

'Hardly ever,' he agreed in steely tones.

Lucasta caught her lower lip betwen her teeth, looking very young and vulnerable. 'I'm sorry you had to have me again,' she blurted out, 'but Marion and I will do our best to stay out of your way.'

His head shot round to look at his niece. 'Marion? How come you're so highly favoured?'

Lucasta managed a tired smile. 'The impertinence of youth,' she said. 'I didn't bother to ask her, but she can hardly go on being Miss Shirley if we're to have any fun together.'

'Brat,' her uncle said with real affection. 'What makes you think I didn't ask to have you?'

Lucasta's eyes shone. 'Did you?'

'Yes, I did. I thought you'd be better off roughing it in the desert with me than sitting in that house in London waiting for your eighteenth birthday. Besides, you're old enough now to keep out of my way when

29

I'm working. I won't have my routine disturbed—even for you!'

'Tell that to Marion,' Lucasta laughed at him. 'Isn't that what she's here for? That's what Mother told her, along with her usual lecture not to get ideas about snaring her defenceless little brother.'

'And how did you take that?' Gregory asked Marion drily, drumming on the back of the front seat with his fingers.

Marion sat up very straight. 'I wondered that your sister should think it necessary under the circumstances.'

'What circumstances?' he asked blandly.

Lucasta said calmly, 'She means Judith!'

'Oh, that!' Her uncle sounded more than a little amused. 'You ought to know, Miss Shirley, that Judith Cameron is a friend of my sister's. I see her sometimes when I'm in London, but any plans for our marriage remain strictly in the fertile imagination of my sister Felicity.'

'But, Gregory, you have to admit you said Judith is the most luscious piece Mother has found you yet. She dotes on you, you know she does!' Lucasta challenged him.

'She's charming,' Gregory smiled.

'Don't you love her at all?' Lucasta pressed him, disappointed.

'I enjoyed her company—in London. Hothouse flowers should never be transplanted from their own environment, though. Their brilliant colours fade and even their perfume is apt to disappoint.'

Lucasta chuckled. 'Poor Judith. I hope you let her down lightly?'

'That, infant, is something you'll never know. I fancy we understand one another.'

I'll bet! Marion thought. She forgot that she hadn't liked the sound of Judith Cameron when she had been told about her in London, and burned with indignation

30

on her behalf. Apparently Gregory Randall didn't care whom he hurt as long as he got what he wanted. Well, he needn't look at her! In fact he'd better not come anywhere near her, or she'd teach him a lesson he wouldn't forget in a hurry!

'Are you getting out, Miss Shirley?'

Marion started and leaped to her feet, hitting her head on top of the door. 'I didn't mean for you to call me Miss Shirley all the time,' she mumbled, confused by the inelegance of her arrival.

'I can wait until you ask me to be less formal,' he taunted her. 'Have you your passport? They'll need it at the desk for tonight. You'll get it back tomorrow before we leave.'

She surrendered it without a murmur, hardly aware that she had done so, for there, directly opposite the entrance to the hotel, was a complete Roman theatre, looking magnificent in the floodlighting.

'Is that real?' she asked dreamily.

'Of course,' Gregory said. 'Amman is a very old city. It's the Rabbath Ammon of the Bible, the capital of the Ammonites. It was when David sent Joab against the Ammonites that he arranged to have Uriah the Hittite killed in the heat of the battle so that he could seize his wife Bath-Sheba for himself. Then Alexander the Great came this way; and the Romans, and the city came to be known as Philadelphia, the City of Brotherly Love. And then in modern times King Abdullah, the present King's grandfather, made it his capital and called it Amman.'

'Oh yes,' said Marion, smiling, 'I remember now. Moses went up against Bashan, and Og came out against him. "For only Og king of Bashan remained of the remnant of giants; behold his bedstead was a bedstead of iron; is it not in Rabbath of the children of Ammon? Nine cubits was the length thereof, and four cubits the breadth of it—"'

'Highly exaggerated, no doubt,' Gregory cut her off.

31

He put his hand beneath her elbow and hurried her up the steps and into the hotel.

'You would think so! ' she said crossly. 'I don't suppose you believe in giants—'

He put his hand on the top of her head. 'Nor in the power of the little people! ' he assured her. 'Go and sit down over there with Lucasta and I'll see about our rooms and order some drinks for us. What will you have? '

She eyed him thoughtfully, about to protest at this overbearing behaviour. Instead, she shrugged. 'I'll have a fruit juice,' she said.

'Nothing stronger? '

She shook her head. She walked across the reception area to where a number of tables were laid out, each one surrounded by its complement of chairs. Lucasta had already chosen a seat facing the entrance and Marion sat down opposite her, pushing her chair back into position after the rough handling it had received at Gregory's hands.

'Mother would be pleased with you,' Lucasta told her with an impudent grin. 'One would almost think you didn't like him.'

'You've all spoilt him,' Marion repressed her. 'It's quite obvious no one has said no to him about anything all his life. No one should have their own way all the time.'

The first indication she had that he might have overheard her was when he slapped her drink down in front of her and sat down negligently between the two girls. She turned her face away from the steely glint in his navy-blue eyes, hoping that he would ignore her.

'I've booked you into adjoining rooms with a bathroom to yourselves. I'm just down the corridor if there's anything either of you want.'

'Thank you,' said Marion, still not looking at him.

'What could we want? ' Lucasta demanded. 'We're not helpless! '

'You might find a scorpion in the bath,' he said casually.

Marion looked at him then all right. *A scorpion?* That she could not face by herself. She couldn't even face up to a tiny spider that she knew wouldn't do her any harm, let alone a scorpion!

'Do you get many scorpions in your castle?' she asked him in a voice that trembled. 'Or any other creepy-crawlies?'

'I've learned to cope with them,' he answered. 'No doubt it's been good for me to have to fend for myself. Insects are no respecters of persons.'

'I don't think I could,' Marion confessed, swallowing hard. She suspected he was getting his own back, but she couldn't be quite sure. He couldn't have known that the mere sight of a spider was enough to reduce her to jelly.

'Well, you only have to call and I'll come,' he said, and his mouth relaxed into a blinding smile that caught her well below the ribs and made her wonder if it was only the thought of scorpions and their like that could knock the stuffing out of her.

Marion had to admit that Gregory Randall had looked after their comfort pretty well. She couldn't fault the standard of their rooms, or the appetising dinner that was served to them in the dining-room downstairs. He had even waited patiently while she and Lucasta had exclaimed over the souvenirs that were on sale in the small boutique at the foot of the stairs. Lucasta had wanted to buy everything in sight, including an elaborate model of the Golden Mosque in Jerusalem, the Dome of the Rock, where Abraham is believed to have made his sacrifice to the Lord, and the place from which the Prophet Mohammed made is nocturnal ascent into Paradise. Marion gently dissuaded her, turning her attention to the carved figures in olive wood made by the Christian Arabs of Bethlehem.

'But I want something from Amman,' Lucasta had protested. ' I've quite made up my mind! '

'Then you'd better think what it is going to be over dinner,' Gregory had insisted. And it had been he, in the end, who had chosen a small piece of Bedouin jewellery for them both, and who had paid for them too.

Indeed, Marion was quite sorry in the morning when Gregory brought his Toyota Landcruiser round to the front of the hotel, telling his niece to wipe the sleep out of her eyes as, while it did feel like six o'clock to her, in his book it was already gone eight and it was time for them to be away.

By daylight, Amman looked even more untidy than the night before. Small specialised shops lined the fantastically steep streets that climbed up and down the seven main hills of the city. In places there were breaks in the houses to reveal a sandy cliff which had not yet been built up, and everywhere there were television aerials receiving not only Jordanian programmes, but from Syria, Lebanon, Israel, and Saudi Arabia as well. Marion thought the disordered charm of the place was an elusive quality that she would never be able to describe to her mother when she wrote to her. What could one say? That here one could still look into the crowded shops and see tailors making bespoke suits, and shoemakers actually making shoes by hand in their doorways. It lent an old-fashioned note to streets that were as remote from the supermarkets and department stores of the West, as was the almost complete absence of women from the scene.

It didn't take them long to leave Amman and Zerqa, the only industrial town in the country, behind them. Ahead stretched the desert turned to gold in the early sunlight, though the soil was more pink than brown or yellow in colour, and this was intensified in the distant hills, slashed by blue and purple shadows which gave away how far away they really were. It seemed one could see for miles in any direction. Mile upon endless

34

mile of wilderness: no wonder the desert was supposed to be so satisfying to the spirit.

'One day I'll show you the more famous Desert castles,' Gregory told them. 'Qasr Amra, and Qasr el Azraq, where Lawrence of Arabia had his headquarters for a while, while he was waiting to go on to Damascus. But today I think we'll go straight home to my Qasr el Biyara. Okay?'

Even Lucasta agreed to this plan, though the sight of the desert had oppressed her spirits. Her mother had been right about one thing. The castle was certainly miles from anywhere and she couldn't for the life of her think what they were going to do with themselves when they got there.

'What does El Biyara mean?' Marion asked, turning the title over in her mind.

'The Castle of Cisterns. It was originally built by the Nabateans, who carved out the city of Petra. They were the masters of irrigation and invented terracing to get better use out of the land. Our water is still drawn from one of the cisterns at the castle. It's as good now as it was then.'

But when Marion first saw the castle all she was aware of was the bitter feeling of disappointment. It looked so insignificant. They came to a gate that was so neglected and rusty that she wondered it opened at all. A small boy heard the Landcruiser coming and ran ahead of them to drag the heavy iron doors apart, catching the coin Gregory tossed to him with a flashing hand. There was no road after that, just a track that bounced from boulder to boulder as they progressed up a faint incline towards a building that had settled into the sand like a hen into her nest. Some of the walls had broken down into rubble, others were still surmounted by a series of little domes that surrounded the main part of the building, the roof of which was not peaked, but rounded, giving the appearance of sausages lying side by side in a frying pan.

'It isn't a castle at all!' Lucasta exclaimed. 'It hasn't even got a garden.' She didn't try to hide her disappointment at the sight of her temporary home. She pointed at a tuft of green stuff that might have been some kind of grass. 'Is that all you can grow?'

Her uncle grinned at her. 'What did you expect, an oasis like Lawrence's castle at Azraq?'

'No, but you said the Nabateans were gardeners—'

'Wait until you see inside,' he bade her. He turned his head towards Marion, his disapproving look falling into place as his eyes met hers. 'Are you disappointed too?' he demanded. She shook her head. 'Why not?' he jeered at her.

'Why do you want me to be?' she countered. 'Is it very beautiful inside?' she added on a sudden inspiration.

'I think so,' he admitted. 'Come in and see for yourself.'

Her legs were stiff after sitting for so long, first in the aeroplane the day before, and then in the Landcruiser that morning. She wished that she could throw a leg over the edge of the vehicle in the same way that he did, but her legs were not nearly long enough and she was forced to jump down from what seemed to be a great height, knowing that he was waiting for her to fall and make a fool of herself. She cast him a childish look of triumph as she landed safely on both feet and felt annoyed at the answering flash of amusement in his eyes.

'I was beginning to think I'd have to fetch a stepladder,' he mocked her.

She laughed with him. 'You cast aspersions on my lack of inches at your peril,' she warned him. 'I'm very sensitive about it.'

'Why?' he said, genuinely surprised. 'Everything about you is in perfect proportion, so why should you care? If anything it adds to your charms.'

Her mouth fell open in astonishment. 'Don't be

silly! ' she rebuked him.

'But it's true,' he declared. 'That fragile daintiness was the first thing I noticed about you. I think most men would find it attractive—but I suspect you know that very well! '

'There's nothing in the least fragile about me! ' she retorted, as angry as she was embarrassed. 'I've always been as tough as they come! '

He raised his eyebrows and she knew that he was laughing at her and that made her crosser than ever. 'Miss Shirley, you've got to be kidding! '

'And don't call me Miss Shirley! ' she snapped. 'At least, not like that! I know you don't like me—'

'Who's being silly now? ' he taunted her. 'Come on inside, Marion. I have something rather special to show you! '

She saw that Lucasta had gone ahead, running over the rough ground, intent on being the first to see where her uncle had chosen to live. Marion followed more slowly, stepping through the heavily studded door into the dim interior with a feeling that she was going forth to meet her destiny and that the dye had been cast long, long before that it was here that something momentous was going to happen to her.

'Through here,' Gregory urged her, breaking the spell of fearful anticipation she had woven around herself. 'These used to be the rooms where the Emirs and their courtiers relaxed in the evenings. There! What do you think of that? '

Marion looked about her with total belief. The walls were covered with the most stunning frescoes she had ever seen. Here was a young girl, beautiful in her nakedness, emerging from her bath; there was a hunting scene, with a hawk about to swoop on its frightened prey; and on the third wall a feast was in progress, the men elaborately robed, the women scarcely clad at all as they danced before their masters.

'Well? ' he demanded. 'Well, what do you think? '

37

She put her hands up to her face. 'Oh, Gregory!' she breathed. 'They're gorgeous! How I wish my father could have seen them!'

CHAPTER III

'Can you do it?'

It was the second time he had asked her, but still Marion hesitated. 'I thought it was contrary to the Moslem religion to depict living creatures?' she said aloud.

'That came later than when these were executed,' he answered impatiently. 'It was forbidden because it was thought to be imitating the work of the Creator. In Moghul India, though, it was encouraged for the very same reason. What about it, Marion? Can you do anything to preserve them? They need quite a bit of restoration work done on them too. Can you do it?'

'I think so,' she said. 'I can clean them. I can't promise to do more than that.' She peered anxiously at a piece of the wall in front of her. 'You ought to get an expert—'

'I have. I got you.'

'I've done similar work with my father,' she encouraged herself, chewing her lower lip thoughtfully. 'But I've never been *responsible*—I'd never forgive myself if I did anything to harm them!'

Gregory came and stood beside her. 'I didn't pick you blind,' he said. 'I made a few enquiries about you before I'd ever seen you—'

'From my mother, I suppose?'

He nodded. 'And from some of your father's colleagues. The results were pretty favourable or you wouldn't be standing here now.'

Her eyes widened. 'You mean you believe I can do it?'

'Don't you?'

He seemed incredibly tall. Of course he didn't believe in giants, he was one himself!

'But what about Lucasta?' she asked him.

'Give her something to do,' he advised. 'I'll see what I can do about finding her some other playmates to amuse her while she's here. Perhaps Denise will oblige —' He broke off as the sound of female laughter rang through the castle. 'Speak of the devil,' he murmured. 'I didn't know she was coming over today, but perhaps it's just as well. You had to get to know each other sooner or later.'

Hurrying, high-heeled footsteps came running towards them and a second later a tall, blonde-haired girl stood in the doorway.

'Are you surprised to see me, *chéri*?' she asked in prettily accented English. She pouted her full lips like a naughty schoolgirl. 'I know you said not before next weekend, but I was lonely without you. I wanted to see for myself this art woman you are bringing here. Is this she? But you are playing some game with me! I do not believe that this one is interested only in stupid pictures!'

'Believe what you like,' Gregory replied, sounding amused. 'Did you come alone?'

'No, I brought the English engineer with me to meet your niece, Lucasta.' She put her hand on Gregory's arm, spreading possessive fingers along his sleeve. 'You need not look like that, with the disapproving mouth! Surely you would prefer he takes an interest in Lucasta than he does so in me?'

Gregory didn't bother to answer her. 'The art woman, as you call her, is called Marion Shirley. Marion, this is Denise Dain. She lives in Beirut, but since Papa presented her with her own aeroplane the world has become her oyster.'

'Why shouldn't he give me my own plane?' the French girl smiled up at him. 'He approves of you, darling, but he likes me to come and see you.'

'But not alone,' he reminded her, the caustic note in his voice betraying the fact that they had argued about that before.

'He is old-fashioned,' Denise admitted. 'He likes you, darling, but he would like you much better when I have your ring safely on my finger.'

Another potential fiancée, Marion noted. Somehow she felt much less sorry for Denise than she had for the rejected Judith in London.

'You wouldn't care for me as a husband,' Gregory said easily. 'The forbidden fruit has far greater attractions—for us both.'

Denise was pleased by the idea and looked it. 'Hush, you will shock Miss Shirley. I am sure *she* would never chase after a man as I do after you!' She turned to Marion, her eyes as hard as pebbles. 'Would you fly hundreds of miles to spend a single hour with Gregory?'

'Hundreds? No.' Marion made a play of considering the matter further. 'I might fly from Beirut.'

'To see me, or to see my frescoes?' Gregory asked lazily.

Her laughter surfaced and burst like a bubble between them. 'What do you think?'

The corners of his mouth kicked up into a wintry smile. 'I think I could be tempted to try and change your mind if you look at me like that!'

Denise's fingers tightened on his arm. 'You are not to flirt with the art woman when I am here, Gregory,' she admonished him. 'It makes me very jealous!'

He laughed down at her. 'You don't know what the word means,' he told her. 'That comes of having every man in the Middle East plotting to get his share of your company.'

Denise pouted. 'You make me sound like a *fille de joie*, and I'm not! Me, I am very respectable!'

'Your father sees to that!' he agreed drily. 'Come, we'd better join the others and see what my niece and your engineer are getting up to.'

Even if there had been no frescoes, Marion would have delighted in the castle. The room Gregory had chosen to make his sitting-room was large with a vaulted roof supported by some pleasing arches, all of them decorated with inscriptions in the Arabic script. Later, Gregory was to tell her that they were later than the walls they decorated and were in the style known as Floriated Kufic, which probably originated in Egypt towards the end of the eighth century. A number of rugs lay higgledy-piggledy on the polished tiles that formed the floor, and some very English easy chairs complete with William Morris patterned covers stood here and there round the room. Marion wondered where they could have come from. Was it possible that he had had them shipped out from England himself?

Lucasta, looking smug and well pleased with herself, preened herself and sat a little closer to the young man who was talking to her, making sure that his attention remained on her and did not drift away to anyone else —Denise Dain in particular. Marion was amused to notice that Lucasta was sufficiently like her uncle to be quite sure of herself where the opposite sex was concerned. She doubted if it would ever occur to either of them that to some people they might prove to be less than wholly desirable.

She shook the young man's hand without him even looking at her and found out that his name was Gaston Brieve and that he was helping to build a bridge somewhere in the Lebanon.

'I come down here quite a bit with Denise,' he proffered shyly. 'But I don't have to rely on her transport. I can come down by car in a few hours most weekends, that is, if Mr Randall doesn't mind?'

Lucasta fluttered her eyelashes and said her uncle would be charmed to see him any time he chose to visit them. Marion began to worry that Lucasta wasn't going to prove to be quite a handful and she wondered exactly what he duties as chaperon were going to entail. She turned impulsively towards Gregory, only to find that he was watching her closely, his mouth as disapproving as she had ever seen it. What she had been about to say to him went completely out of her mind.

'Can you read those inscriptions?' she asked instead.

'No,' he answered her. 'They are more or less indecipherable, but it doesn't present the problem one would suppose. Koranic inscriptions are not there to be read but to create an awareness of the divine presence.'

'How strange,' she murmured.

He stood up, his eyes still holding hers. 'Would you like to see your room? We'll be having lunch soon and I expect you'd like to tidy up first. Lucasta seems to have found her own way around.'

Marion rose too. 'She's very much at home,' she agreed.

Gregory's glance mocked her. 'Gaston won't do her any harm,' he said.

'I hope not. She's very young.'

'And you don't approve of her holding hands with a comparative stranger?' he finished for her. 'Isn't that a little prudish?'

Marion wished he didn't have the effect of making her feel like a cat whose fur he was stroking the wrong way. It gave her an agitated feeling that distressed her, and she didn't like him any better because of it.

'I feel responsible for her. It's why I'm here after all.'

'Partly,' he acknowledged. His eyes swept over her and came back to her face. 'Lucasta can look after herself, my dear—probably better than you can.'

He led the way down a long corridor and threw open the door of a room at the far end. 'Lucasta is in the other wing with me,' he told her. 'I thought you might like to get away from us every now and then. Nobody will disturb you here.'

She had to admit it was a very pleasant room. It was simply furnished with an iron bedstead and a plywood cupboard for her clothes, but its walls too had once

43

been decorated with frescoes, though they had not survived nearly as well as the others she had seen. These were smoke-blackened and had been scribbled on by passing visitors with disastrous results.

' Who would have had a fire in here? ' she demanded, running her finger-tips over the black soot.

' The Bedu. A man and his two wives were in residence here when I came. I moved them into one of the outbuildings and provide them with proper heating and food. In return, the two women take it in turns to cook for me.'

Marion tried to keep the shock his words had given her to herself. ' Do they speak English? ' she managed to ask.

' The man manages a few words—mostly Glubb Pasha, whom he says he knew well. He claims he got his gun from him and is never to be seen without it. He has a rather bloodthirsty appearance, but he's never shot anyone yet, to my knowledge. If you're afraid of him, stay out of his way, because if he guesses that you're nervous of him his feelings will be hurt. He has a very high opinion of the British.'

Marion was willing to bet with herself that no one within a hundred miles was as dangerous as the man beside her, and then she caught herself wondering why she thought so and was rather glad that he couldn't read her thoughts. She went over to the window and found to her surprise that it didn't look out over the desert, but over a small, enclosed garden that was bright with flowers and running water.

' I shall need quite a few supplies before I can start cleaning the frescoes,' she said, suddenly afraid that he might follow her and box her in against the window. ' You should have told me in Amman and I could have given you a list of what I'll need.'

' I'll get Denise to fly them down from Beirut.'

She raised an eyebrow, looking down at her hands. ' Doesn't she mind being your messenger boy? '

He chuckled. 'Messenger girl, please! She hasn't raised any objections so far. We understand one another very well, I believe, and she likes to give pleasure—'

'I'm sure she does!' Marion agreed warmly.

'There are worse ambitions,' he said, his eyes very lazy beneath his dark brows. He stretched out a hand and she winced away from him, her skin smarting with nervous anticipation of his touch. He pushed open the window with a malicious little smile and pointed through it to the flame tree that graced the far corner of the garden. 'What are yours, Miss Shirley?'

'I don't know,' she admitted.

He bent his head. 'Then why condemn those who do?'

She opened her eyes wide. 'I don't. Your morals are your own affair!'

His eyes glinted. 'Remember that, Marion Shirley, and we'll get along very well.' He stepped away from her. 'Fear and ignorance lie behind most instant condemnations. It makes one wonder what I could have done to frighten you. Perhaps when we know one another better you'll tell me?'

Not if she could help it! Marion threw back her head to show him that she didn't care what he said, but she couldn't quite meet his eyes. She supposed it was a kind of cowardice, but she would have done anything at that moment to get rid of him, out of her room as quickly as possible.

'Mr Randall, would you mind if I experimented with the frescoes in here first?' she said loudly.

'It was Gregory when I showed you the other frescoes,' he reminded her. He looked about the room, his legs slightly apart and his hands on his hips. 'This room was part of the women's quarters, which makes the subject matter of many of the frescoes rather—startling, shall we say? I hope they won't shock you.'

She forgot her anger with him and laughed. 'I have

45

seen the naked female form before, Mr Randall,' she said demurely.

He gave her an appreciative smile. ' I don't doubt it,' he mocked her. ' Will you bring the list of what you need to the lunch table? It's still winter, and the weather is rather unsettled. I'd rather Denise got away well before dark.'

She nodded. She could hardly wait for him to shut the door behind him, before flinging herself on to the bed. She was seldom tired, and she refused to admit that she was tired now, but the strain of having Gregory Randall in the same room with her had told on her nerves and had left her feeling as flat as a pancake. The less she saw of him while she was here the better, she thought. She would concentrate on those glorious frescoes and spend all the rest of her time with Lucasta. It sounded a very satisfactory programme and she hugged herself with glee. Imagine it, the wonder of it, to make those pictures come to life again, to restore their colours to their original singing hues, and to piece together the parts that were missing with the same delicate touch that her father had taught her so painstakingly in Greece.

She looked about the room, trying to make the shadowy figures on the wall come alive. Only some of them were women, she discovered. The rest, in various stages of fright, seemed to be trying to rush across a narrow bridge which was held by devils equally intent on throwing them off, down into the abyss on either side. Could this be someone's idea of the Entrance of Paradise? It seemed likely, for, in another place, massed soldiers were advancing, their war wounds very much in evidence, apparently certain of their place in heaven. So the women were the ever-virgin houris who would add to their delights throughout eternity, Marion decided, and was annoyed to discover that Gregory Randall had been right. The frankness of the pictures had shocked her after all, not for what they revealed, but more because of the attitude of mind they implied. It was not her idea of paradise to spend her eternity beneath the soles of her husband's feet, if she were lucky enough to be there at all. Yet had the Christians of the time given their women a better deal? Not if the evidence of St Anthony, cowering away from the evils of womankind in the desert, could be believed.

After a while she sat on the edge of the bed and wrote out her list of requirements. She hoped Denise would be able to get the things she wanted and that she wouldn't have to send home to her mother for some of them. Water seemed to be in plentiful supply, and it would probably be possible to buy a soda-less soap, but she was less certain about the chemicals. Aceticum anhydricane, barium hydroxide and pyridinum all were essential for what she wanted to do. She wrote them down, and then wrote them down again in capital letters in case Denise couldn't read her writing.

Then, even though she knew they were probably all waiting to start lunch, she took a last look at the faded frescoes, arguing with herself exactly how she was going to tackle their restoration. First she thought she would begin in one place and then in another, and then she noticed the small, shy-looking *houri* in the corner of the room who had something familiar about her, though quite what it was Marion couldn't decide. She would begin with her, she decided, because she felt an immediate sympathy with her. She knew just how she felt with all those soldiers marching into heaven. She, too, would have hidden in a corner under the circumstances and hope to be overlooked. That was how she felt when Gregory Randall stood over her, looking down at her with that superior air of his, his mouth a tight line of disapproval. Not that Gregory would want her, but the poor little *houri* couldn't have been as certain of escaping the horrible fate in store for her.

A knock at the door broke into her day-dream and Marion opened the door to the bundle of cheap black material on the other side. A pair of gleaming, blue-grey eyes peered curiously through the veil that hung from her head down her back and which she had pulled across to half-hide her face. Marion sought for some kind of greeting in her mind and came out with, '*Marhaba.* Hullo.'

The woman looked blank, producing a shy greeting of her own, and beckoned, palm downwards, for Marion to follow her into the dining-room.

'Ah, Zein—I beg her pardon, Umm Haroun! The birth of her son is too recent for me to have got used to her new name!—she found you all right?'

'Yes,' Marion smiled. 'I thought *marhaba* meant hullo in Arabic, but she didn't seem to understand me.'

'The Bedouin dialect is very different from the Arabic that the Palestinians speak, for example. Unless they can speak both they don't understand each other at all.'

'And you speak both?' Marion said, knowing the answer even as she asked the question.

'A little.'

Marion took her seat at the table. 'Are all the original Jordanians Bedouin?' she wanted to know.

He shrugged. 'Most of them, I suppose. Those who are not Circassians, or Druses, or Samaritans, or the descendants of the Crusaders, most of whom are still Christians.'

'*Samaritans*?' Marion gasped. 'Like the Good Samaritan in the Bible?'

'Like him, and like the woman at the well,' he confirmed. 'Nothing much changes around here except on the surface.'

Lucasta nudged Marion's arm. 'You should have been here earlier,' she whispered. 'Gregory had to find some knives and forks for us himself! He doesn't bother when he's by himself, but Denise insisted.'

Marion looked round the table and wondered how he managed without some kind of cutlery. A great pile of flat bread had been placed in the centre of the

48

table and was surrounded by bowls of different substances that made her mouth water to look at them.

'One has standards! ' Denise declared forcefully. 'It is not good to be a savage, *mon ami*, as Papa would soon tell you.'

'Indeed, he would,' Gregory agreed. 'But when in Rome, I like to do as the Romans do. A knife and fork adds nothing to the taste of the food.' He turned lazy, dark blue eyes on to Marion's face. 'What do you think? '

'I'd like to know how to do it properly,' she admitted.

Denise raised her eyes heavenwards. 'But what is properly? ' she muttered. 'It is known that the French cuisine is the best in the world, therefore— ' She picked up her knife and fork, leaving the rest of her sentence to their imagination.

Gaston nodded across the table at her. 'Knives and forks for French cuisine are a necessity, but nobody would describe this as French cuisine! ' He too picked up a fork and waved it in the air to make his point.

Zein, the Mother of Haroun, apparently understood too, for she picked out a fork from the pile on the table and offered it to Marion, nodding towards the food.

'*Laa*! ' Gregory roared at her. He took the fork in his own hand and put it back on the table. He tore off a portion of bread and dipped it into one of the bowls, putting it against Marion's lips. 'Open wide! ' he bade her, and popped it into her mouth.

'What is it? ' she demanded as the strange taste broke across her tongue.

'That one is ground up chick-peas with olive oil. Try one of those little meat balls and with it this dip of yoghourt and lemon juice.' He smiled with satisfaction at her delighted pleasure, and said something in her own language to Zein, who giggled and shyly turned away from the table.

'What did you say to her? ' Marion asked him, her

49

face alight with laughter.

'I said if you had been brought up on her cooking you might have grown into a large lady—'

'That has nothing to do with it,' Marion retorted. 'It's all in one's genes, I'm sure of it. But if all the food is like this I will go back to England a good deal fatter than when I came!'

He laughed too. 'It's difficult to be moderate when everything is new,' he agreed. 'If you will accept a little advice, leave a little space for the next course, which is the traditional Bedouin dish of *Mansef*. This is only meant to be the hors d'oeuvres.'

'Goodness,' said Marion.

She was glad she had followed his advice though when Umm Haroun cleared away the first course and brought in an enormous dish of rice, mixed with roast nuts and pine seeds, with a lavish quantity of lamb on top.

'*Mansef* means literally "a big dish",' Gregory said drily, enjoying the expressive wonder on her face. 'Perhaps, for this, you'd better use a fork,' he added.

It was terribly good. The vision she had had of herself being forced to eat the eye of the animal that had been conjured up by his telling her that this was a traditional Bedouin dish receded, and Marion set to with a will and ate one of the most enormous meals ever to have come her way, despite Gregory's open amusement at the extent of her appetite.

'Do you always eat as well as this?' she asked him.

'Zein is a better cook than Umm Hamid, as her husband will be the first to tell you, but they both do me very well.'

'It is always the same,' Denise agreed. 'I enjoy it when I come here, but for everyday it is dull to the palate. When I come for longer than one day I do most of the cooking myself. I worry about Gregory's digestion when I'm not here. He eats too many eggs, which is very bad for the liver.'

Marion was suddenly aware of the implications that lay behind the French girl's remarks. Did she often stay for days together at the castle? And, if she did, was it so that she could be alone with Gregory Randall? The idea distressed her. It wasn't that she minded what Gregory did, but if Denise took it into her head to come while she and Lucasta were there it would be almost impossible to ignore the situation.

Gregory rubbed his chin against his knuckles before lighting himself a cigarette. 'Monsieur Dain likes to retreat to the desert every now and then. Denise caters for his tastes as much as for her own.'

'And you, *mon cher*, do you pretend that you are not pleased when I take a hand in the kitchen?' Denise challenged him. 'You are not so different! You cannot pretend to me, for me, I know better!'

'Then you have answered yourself,' he teased her. He patted her hand that was lying on the table. 'I am tempted to ask you to to make the coffee, but Zein will want to serve her own brew in the sitting-room. She is always in a hurry these days with her little son to feed as well as us.'

'Why doesn't Umm Hamid do all your cooking for the time being?' Gaston asked his host.

Gregory grinned. 'Abou Hamid likes a peaceful household. The women quarrel if they don't have the same opportunities for turning an honest penny. And also, I have to admit that I prefer Zein's gentle touch on my crockery. Umm Hamid has a very heavy hand when it comes to the washing-up.'

'Abou Hamid,' Marion repeated. 'Does that mean the Father of Hamid?'

'Hamid is his eldest son. His own name is Mohammed, but he is hardly ever called by it.'

Marion found herself looking with greater interest at Zein when she served them their coffee, wondering what it was like to share her husband with another woman, a woman moreover older than herself who had

51

borne her husband a son when Zein was still at home learning the household tasks of being a wife and mother in her father's home. She noticed that the girl had dyed her eyelids with black *kohl*, an effect not very far removed from the eye-shadow she used herself. Her face bore none of the tattoo marks that Marion had read were popular with some of the Bedouin tribes, but she had dyed her nails and the palms of her hands with henna, probably as a hygienic measure, for henna is considered to have many of the same properties as an antiseptic solution has in the West. Then, it was not exactly a veil she was wearing, more a large scarf which completely covered the sides of her face and was crossed over under her chin to keep it out of the way. The voluminous black robe that covered her from head to foot was at least a yard longer than she was, and was pulled up over a wide, elaborately decorated belt that matched her glass and copper beads and bangles that completed her outfit. It was strange to meet someone, to think one had made a genuine contact, and yet to know so little about that person and perhaps even less about how she lived out her days.

The Bedu girl looked back at her with a much more open curiosity. She touched her lips and giggled, admiring the lipstick that Marion wore. If her husband approved, Marion vowed to herself, she would give Zein one of hers, the colour of which would suit her honey-coloured skin better than it did her own rain-washed, English pink and white complexion.

At last Denise reluctantly got up to go. She made no bones about the warmth with which she embraced Gregory, making soft, purring sounds in his neck, and promising to be back the following Friday, with or without her father as there were now other women at the castle.

'You are to miss me more each day I'm gone,' she instructed him with a soft, intimate smile. 'And you are not to flirt with the art woman! It is understood?'

'If you bring the things she needs to restore the frescoes, we'll both be too busy working to see much of each other,' he told her.

'Then I shall certainly bring them.' She turned away from him, her eyes wet with tears, and bade the others a casual *au revoir*. 'But where is Gaston? I cannot go without him!'

The young engineer presented a rather pink face. 'I was saying goodbye to Lucasta,' he explained uneasily. He squared his shoulders and held out his hand to Gregory. 'I shall bring the car next time. There are many places your niece should see while she's here if you have no objection, *monsieur*?'

'Not if you check with Miss Shirley or myself first. When can we expect you?'

'Would next Thursday evening be too soon? We get off early on Thursdays to give the workmen a chance to go home for the Friday prayer. I might be rather late arriving, but there would be no need for anyone to wait up for me. I can let myself in.'

'Do that. The door is never locked,' Gregory assured him easily.

They all went outside to see the French couple go. The plane looked small and not very robust to Marion's critical eyes, but Denise pulled on her helmet and disappeared into the cockpit with an engaging assurance. A moment later the Piper was bobbing over the rough ground as it taxied into position to take off.

'She must be very brave!' Marion exclaimed after the heart-stopping moment when the aeroplane left the ground and climbed up into the air.

'Or foolhardy,' Gregory said drily. 'To be brave, you have to first know what fear is.'

'And Denise doesn't?'

He shook his head. 'She's armour-plated with Papa's money. But one day she's going to find herself and then she'll be a rather marvellous person.'

And then he'll marry her, Marion thought, and she

wondered why the idea should be so objectionable to her. Was it only because she thought that even Gregory Randall deserved someone better than the going-to-be-marvellous Denise Dain? She hoped not, because if she did think that it had to be because she liked him a great deal better than she had yet admitted to herself.

CHAPTER IV

Marion settled into her new life with an ease that surprised her. She saw very little of Gregory except at mealtimes, but she was more than content to explore the local terrain with Lucasta and came to enjoy her encounters with the local people whose hospitality was apparently endless and whose curiosity about the strangers in their midst could never be sufficiently satisfied. Whenever he had nothing better to do, which was most of the time, Abou Hamid followed them about, pretending to translate their remarks to all and sundry. But he had little English himself. He showed them his guns with pride, claiming that one had been given to him by Glubb Pasha, and another by the King himself. He also wanted to know all about their relations and if they visited their uncles and aunts and cousins with a frequency he considered proper. Marion enjoyed these exchanges, but she tried to keep them to a minimum because it made Lucasta edgy to be asked about her parents' doings and she considered his questions about them to be grossly impertinent.

' Why does he want to know? ' she kept asking. ' He'll be asking you next how much you earn teaching at school! '

' He already has,' Marion told her. She had answered him too, but that she did not pass on to Lucasta. Nor did she tell her that his two wives had been listening to the whole conversation, demanding that he should translate every word for their benefit, and how they had apparently understood that she valued her independence. They too, they had told her, were not afraid to entertain men as equals when their husband was away, but when he was there it was better that the men should be left to their own talk, they preferred to gossip to other women about the things that really mattered. It was nice to have both, Marion had pointed out, and the women had gravely nodded their consent before they had asked her about Gregory's reasons for sending for her from England. In vain had Marion protested that Gregory had had nothing to do with her coming.

By the week-end, though, she was more than ready to start work. Denise, arriving in the early afternoon of Thursday, handed over the chemicals Marion had asked for, warning her to be sparing with them. ' I did not enjoy trailing around Beirut in search of such things. Next time, you had best come back with me and find them for yourself! '

Marion thanked her with as much warmth as she could summon up and took them straight to her room, determined to get started as early as she could the following morning.

She heard Gaston's arrival in the middle of the night in a haze of sleep. She was glad he had come because Lucasta liked him and nobody could have thought that she would ever be in the least bit interested in frescoes. If Marion didn't know by now that she was bored stiff by any kind of painting, she would have been a much worse teacher than she was. Lucasta's idea of getting through the hour devoted to the art class every week had been to turn it into a talking-shop with most of her friends and, providing that they didn't annoy anyone else, Marion had allowed her to do just that.

When Friday dawned, bright and clear, Marion could have hugged herself with excitement. She went into her room immediately after breakfast and shut the door firmly behind her, determined to begin on the shy little *houri* as soon as she had prepared her witch's brew.

The morning passed with a speed that disconcerted her. She had been far more successful than she had hoped and she was bubbling over with glee when she ran down the corridor to the dining-room for lunch.

' May I come and see how you're doing? ' Gregory asked her.

She was reluctant to show him her small beginning. In the most ridiculous way, she felt he would impose on the timidity of the delightful little creature she had so carefully revealed.

'I'm not really ready for visitors,' she said.

He looked disappointed and she relented, her longing to share her excitement with someone who would appreciate what she was doing overcoming her fellow-feeling for her little *houri*.

'Don't expect too much,' she warned him. 'There isn't much to see yet.'

'I won't,' he promised.

It was only then that Marion realised that no one else had turned up for the meal. 'Where are the others?' she asked, a little uncomfortable at being alone with him. 'Why didn't you go with them?'

'Because, like you, I have work to do,' he answered.

She looked down at her plate. 'Denise must have been disappointed,' she remarked.

'I dare say she'll survive,' he murmured with all the heartlessness she expected from him. 'Why don't you like her, Marion?'

'I don't know her well enough to like or dislike her. She's a lovely girl and she seems to have a great deal going for her—'

'But you are not greatly interested in material things, so it can't be that that bothers you.'

'How do you know?' she shot back at him.

His navy-blue eyes regarded her thoughtfully. 'I know.' He was uncannily sure he was right. 'Nor do I think you are jealous of her beauty. You are well enough yourself not to be afraid of any competition she might offer. So why don't you like her?'

'I don't dislike her,' Marion repeated.

'But there is something there?' He hesitated. 'I can't see Denise ever taking anything from you that you really want. She is a girl who has few friends amongst her own sex. Won't you befriend her?'

57

'It takes two to make a friendship,' Marion reminded him tartly. She knew one thing Denise would take if she could and that was Gregory Randall, and he must be blind if he couldn't see it! 'Why don't you ask Denise why she doesn't like me?' she added. He ought to know the answer to that too, she thought. Denise would never like any female who was living under the same roof as Gregory because as far as she was concerned life for women was a competition with man as the prize for the winners, and she couldn't conceive that everyone else didn't share her attitude.

'She's afraid of you,' Gregory answered. 'She thinks you're beautiful and clever, and that you haven't got time for ordinary people like her.'

Marion could imagine her saying that. The impertinence of it might have amused her at another time, but not today. She knew then that Denise was her enemy, and she couldn't remember ever having had an enemy before.

'She should talk to Lucasta,' she said wryly.

'She hasn't Lucasta's confidence, or yours either,' Gregory sighed. 'For all her father wraps her in cotton-wool, she's a very vulnerable person.'

Marion lifted an eyebrow. 'Sensitive,' she shrugged.

He ignored her obvious mockery. 'More young and defenceless. It would be easy to hurt her.'

Marion could only marvel at the blindness of men. In her book, Denise was neither young nor defenceless; she was as tough as old leather and in no need of anyone's care and protection. Still, it was easy to see Gregory had swallowed the bait she had cast in his direction, hook, line and sinker. The only thing Marion couldn't understand was why she should feel hurt on his behalf. She had no reason to suppose he deserved better treatment than he was likely to get at Denise's grasping, possessive hands. Had he worried about Judith's feelings back in London?

'Where is she now?' Marion asked him.

'I persuaded her to go off with Lucasta and Gaston. The three-day week-end wreaks havoc with my work schedule.'

Marion gurgled with delighted laughter. Denise couldn't come as high up on his list of priorities as she had thought if his work still came first with him!

'What's funny about that?' he demanded.

She shook her head at him, breaking into laughter all over again. 'Is the book going well?' she asked in a trembling voice.

'No, it's not! I came here to get away from people, not to have to entertain half the world every week-end!'

'My mother,' Marion told him gently, 'always says it's a mistake to try to escape from the demands of other people. They're more important than our own interests—most of the time.'

His mouth clapped shut into its familiar disapproving line. 'Easy to say when you haven't a deadline to meet,' he growled. 'Are you trying to tell me that I ought to give in to Denise's demands?'

She couldn't bring herself to recommend any such thing. 'Only you can answer that,' she managed to say. 'I don't know what her demands are!'

'And that makes a difference? What about your own demands?'

That shocked the colour out of her cheeks. 'What makes you think I would make any?' she retorted. 'I don't want anything from you Mr Randall.'

The steely glint in his eyes disturbed her. 'Your very presence here makes demands!' His expression relaxed into a smile of unusual warmth. 'It makes me think of all the other things there are to do besides shutting myself up and working.' He leaned back in his chair, watching the mobile features of her face as they reflected her uncertainty and the defensive reaction to his words. 'Have you ever heard of the mosaics of Madaba?'

She nodded, because she had vaguely known that there was a sixth-century mosaic map of Palestine somewhere in Jordan. Her father had spoken of it warmly, she remembered, when he recommended that if she was interested in fine mosaics the best place to see the very finest was in the Bardo Museum in Tunis. 'Except for the Church of St Saviour in Chora, in Istanbul.' he had added. 'But that is something else and not to be compared with what we usually mean by mosaic work.'

'Doesn't it depict Old Jerusalem?' she said now.

He gave a wry smile. 'If you can spare the time, would you like to go and see it this afternoon? We could go on to the Dead Sea afterwards.'

'Could we?' she hesitated. 'Shouldn't we go tomorrow when the others can come too?'

'And listen to Gaston whispering sweet nothings in Lucasta's ear?'

Her eyes opened wide. 'Oh dear, I do hope not. Should I speak to her, do you think?'

'What about?'

Marion stumbled, not knowing how to put it. 'Would Mrs Hartley consider Gaston a suitable friend for Lucasta? She *is* only seventeen.'

'Quit worrying, Marion. You'll only make a fool of yourself if you try to put Lucasta on a leading-rein. Do you want to come with me this afternoon or not?'

'Yes,' she said.

She had forgotten that he had said he was coming to see the results of her morning's work after lunch and she couldn't think why he followed her down the long corridor that led to her room. A light remark might have relieved the atmosphere, but she couldn't make her brain think of anything except the way he towered over her as he walked beside and to wish for the millionth time since she had grown up that she were tall and dignified, and didn't have to skip along beside him, employing three steps for every two of his.

When she opened the door her eyes went straight to the little *houri* she had treated. Her timidity was as familiar as if it were her own.

'What made you begin with her?' Gregory asked, moving in close to look at the little figure the better.

'She appeals to me,' Marion confessed. 'I felt as though I knew her as soon as I saw her.'

Gregory looked amused. 'That's hardly surprising,' he said drily. 'She's a favourite of mine too.'

Marion picked up a brush and touched the *houri's* robe with a loving hand. 'None of those soldiers are going to get her! They'll have to make do with all the others!'

He laughed. He was closer to her than she had thought and she could feel his warm breath on her cheek. She put the brush down hastily, self-conscious in a way she had never been before. It was fortunate that he didn't want to watch her work, she thought. She'd be too nervous to do a thing!

'Funny you should say that,' he said. 'When I first came to see this place I noticed her at once. It's a good thing she's shy, I thought to myself, because that one has to wait for me! Most certainly, those brutish soldiers are not going to have her!'

'You're much less brutish, of course,' Marion murmured with a smile. It was quite a thought to think of Gregory Randall making love to anyone as timid as— the little *houri*, for example. Indeed, she wished the thought had not occurred to her at all, for she had been much better off without it. Yet she couldn't help remembering how warm and firm his lips had been against hers at the airport and she felt a gust of feeling within her that was as real as a body-blow to her solar plexus.

'Perhaps not in intention,' he said with a mocking amusement that made her hope earnestly that he couldn't read her mind. 'She looks very kissable to me.'

'No better than any other pin-up, in fact,' Marion

said, disappointed in him. 'I think she'd be better off with an appreciative soldier, who'd see her as a person, not a sex symbol.'

'She might like being kissed,' he objected. 'Don't you?'

Her experience was much more limited than she wanted to admit, especially as kisses were considered such common currency nowadays. She pinned a smile to her lips.

'Doesn't everyone?'

He put his hands on her shoulders and swung her round to face him, lifting her easily on to the stool she had been using to give her extra height while she worked. Finding herself on his level for once, she found his mouth much less disapproving than she had thought. It was firm and very, very self-assured, but there was nothing condemnatory about it, not even when she made a flustered movement to escape him. *She wasn't ready to be kissed by him*! She heaved a deep breath to try and steady herself, scarcely surprised at all when his hand slipped from her shoulder to the back of her head, drawing her firmly but inevitably into the circle of his embrace. She would have protested even then, but her lips trembled so badly that she thought better of it.

'What a sweet fraud you are, Marion Shirley,' he said softly. 'You're every bit as shy and as fearful as she is, aren't you? No wonder you have such a fellow-feeling for her.'

She hoped she didn't look as ridiculous to him as she felt. 'I didn't know—You took me by surprise!' she defended herself.

His lips met hers in the briefest of contacts and the shock of it reached right down inside her, fountaining up again in a sensation of such warm delight that she could only wonder if she would ever be the same again. She stepped off the stool in a haze of bewilderment and sat down on it quickly in case her knees refused to support her any longer.'

Gregory squatted down beside her, his navy-blue eyes very dark as he looked at her. 'Marion, what's the matter? Are you all right?'

She managed a shadow of her usual smile. 'You shouldn't flirt with the art woman!' she rebuked him.

He smiled back at her, cupping her chin in his hand. 'Why not?'

'Denise told you not to,' she reminded him.

'You'll have to think up a better reason than that,' he murmured.

'What better reason can there be? Don't you want to please Denise?'

'Not to the point of having her tell me what to do. No girl, however pretty, is going to run my life for me,' he said firmly.

She stirred against his restraining hand, seeking to make her escape, but he had no intention of letting her go.

'We'll have to do something about this fixation you have about Denise,' he said against her lips. 'I don't want to hear her name again this afternoon.' He kissed her slowly and all inclination for escape died away. 'There!' he warned her on a note of masculine triumph there was no mistaking. 'I'll claim a similar forfeit—'

'No. No, you won't!' Marion leaped to her feet, not even trying to hide her anger. 'You may have Judith in London, and Denise for week-ends, but you haven't got me! I don't play those sort of games—'

'And you think I do?'

She nodded, unable to speak when she saw the cold mockery on his face. She would have given anything to have banished the dislike she was sure he felt for her.

'One day,' he said, weighing each word with a deliberation that appalled her, 'I'll make you take that back, Miss Shirley. You'll eat your words if you choke on them, and I won't lift a finger to help you!'

'I'm sorry,' she said.

'You haven't begun to be sorry!' He hesitated, aware of the appeal in her wide, anxious eyes. 'I shan't bother you again!'

Marion looked away, struggling with the bitter despair that seized her. 'Are we still going to Madaba?' she asked, afraid he would see the tears that were gathering at the back of her eyes.

'Do you still want to go?'

She nodded. 'I've said I'm sorry,' she whispered.

He watched her for a moment in silence, then he said, 'Don't give it another thought.' He twisted his mouth into a wry smile. 'I'll meet you in ten minutes at the car. You needn't worry about being alone with me,' he added caustically. 'I don't seduce frightened little girls. I prefer a more sophisticated approach!'

'Oh, Gregory, please don't!'

He crossed his arms in front of him and stared at her. 'Don't what? What do you want?'

She blinked, wiping the tears away from her cheeks. 'I'd like to be friends. I didn't mean—'

'Friends?' He sounded as though the word had really stung him on the raw. 'I wonder if you know what you're asking!' He walked over to her and touched her wet cheeks with gentle fingers. 'I'll try, Marion,' he said at last. 'Only don't cry any more and I'll do anything you ask!'

She gulped. 'Thank you,' she said with relief. 'I didn't mean to insult you, Gregory. It was a compliment—in a way—because most women would like you to make love to them, only—'

'Only you don't?' he finished for her.

But she did! She liked it far too much! 'I didn't dislike it,' she compromised, and wondered why he laughed, his face clearing as if by magic. 'But it didn't mean anything, did it?'

'Oh, I wouldn't say that,' he said, and turned on his heel and left her alone with the little *houri* she was re-

64

storing.

Marion made a face at her, admitting to herself that they were two of a kind. ' You can't wait for ever,' she addressed the painted wall. ' He might not come. He might never get to heaven and what will you do then? '

But the *houri* made no answer. Only Marion knew quite well what she would have said if she could. She would have pointed out that Gregory was in the same world as Marion and yet *she* hadn't fared very well either.

' I only *want* to be his friend! ' Marion declared out loud, and flung a cloth at the simpering disbelief on the face of the *houri*. Well, she didn't believe it either! But if she didn't want that what else was it that she did want?

Marion tied her scarf round her head, pulling it so tight that she almost strangled herself. She reached up her hands and began to pull herself up into the front of the Land Cruiser when two strong hands lifted her easily and dumped her on to the canvas-covered seat.

' I've left a message for the others,' Gregory said, ' We won't be back till late.'

Marion said nothing. She clutched the edge of her seat as they set off across the rough ground, her spirits rising by the minute. It was grand to have the sun on her face and the wind pulling at the edges of her scarf.

' How long will it take us to get there? ' she asked as Gregory eased the Land Cruiser through the rusty iron gates.

' To Madaba? More than an hour. To the Dead Sea, rather longer. I thought we'd go by way of Mount Nebo so that you can see where Moses looked down into the Promised Land before he died.'

' The very spot? ' she insisted, sounding doubtful.

' Why not? It wasn't very long ago in the historical perspective of a land like this.'

' Three thousand years,' she pointed out.

'Practically modern times,' he teased her. 'I'm sure if you asked around you'd find someone who remembered him passing through their village.'

'They'll remember you,' she asserted. 'What made you want to live in a castle?'

'It was there I saw the difference the Spaniards were able to make when they restored the frescoes of the most famous of the desert castles, Qasr Amra, and I wanted to do the same for my castle. It's too far out for it to be on the tourist circuit, and there isn't enough money to go round anyway. It seemed almost too good to be true when I heard about you!'

'You used to write to my father,' she said shyly. 'My mother told me so.'

'That didn't mean you had followed in his footsteps. It was Lucasta who told me about your evening classes. My sister could hardly believe her luck when I offered to have Lucasta for the holidays—providing you came along too.'

Marion squinted into the sun. 'That child is left alone far too much,' she said severely. 'Isn't your sister afraid she'll get into trouble?'

'I fancy she feels the risks are less in London than if she were to drag her off to some of the parties she and my brother-in-law go to. Lucasta is too young to keep her head amongst the jet-set just yet.'

'You don't seem to mind if Gaston turns her head. He's quite a bit older than she!'

Gregory grinned. 'He won't do her any harm. He's still wet behind the ears compared to the sort of gentlemen I'm thinking about. Lucasta will run rings round him and he won't even know it. He's a decent enough young fellow.'

'But, at seventeen—'

'Lucasta is as old as Cleopatra compared with her would-be chaperon,' he mocked her. 'You don't have to worry about any niece of mine, Marion.'

But she did have to worry about herself! She sat

back in her seat, half wishing that he would give her something more to worry about. The desert was more beautiful than ever and she amused herself by trying to judge how many miles she could see in any given direction. They met the old King's Highway, the ancient trade route the caravans of old had travelled between Cairo or Mecca in the south, and Damascus, the Lebanon, and even Antioch, which was now the ruined Roman city of Jerash, in the north. The new, modern Desert Highway that cut several hours off the journey went off to the left.

'That's the way to Aqaba,' Gregory told her. 'And to Petra, the "rose-red city half as old as time".'

Petra had been a dream of her childhood, but she had never thought she might go there herself.

'I don't suppose Lucasta would be interested,' she sighed.

'Probably not,' Gregory agreed, too promptly not to be convincing. 'You'll have to get someone else to take you.'

She felt snubbed and supposed she deserved it. 'Have you been there often?' she asked in a small voice.

He turned to look at her. 'Are you asking me to take you?' he said bluntly.

'No, of course not.' She tried to leave it there, but she could not. 'If I asked you, would you take me?' she asked.

'No.'

That hurt more than anything else had done. She tried telling herself that he had his deadline to meet and that he couldn't possibly spare the time to indulge her childhood dreams. He was more than doing his duty by taking her to Madaba.

'I'll talk to Lucasta about it,' she said.

'You won't make me change my mind,' he told her, his voice hard with the dislike she knew he felt for her. 'Petra has long been my dream too, and I won't allow you to spoil it. You might persuade Denise to fly you down there.'

67

'I don't want to go with Denise,' she said childishly. 'If Lucasta doesn't want to go, I won't go at all!'

'Then I wish you luck in persuading her,' he told her. But it wasn't luck he was wishing her. He was hoping that she would never get there, though she didn't stop to ask herself why. The tears burned at the back of her eyes. She had made a mistake in wanting to be friends with him. He was the most hateful creature she had ever met!

'You can't stop me going!' she challenged him, sure that he would if he could.

'I could, but I won't.'

'Just because I'm staying at your castle, it doesn't give you the right to say what I can and can't do!'

'You're staying at the castle as my employee,' he reminded her with crushing emphasis. 'Paying your fare out here and your salary for the next few weeks means that your time belongs to me while you're here and I intend to get good value for my money. Now, for heaven's sake, let's talk about something else!'

He sounded tired and irritable and for the first time she wondered if his book was going badly. Of course he wasn't paying her any salary, Mrs Hartley was doing that, but the temptation to point this out to him was lost in her new anxiety about his work.

'Is that why we're going to Madaba?' she hazarded. 'Is there something about it in your book?'

His smile was bleak. 'Not really, though Madaba is a Christian city. The descendants of the Crusaders were moved there from near Petra. The most famous of the mosaics is in the Greek Orthodox church there.'

'But if it isn't in your book—'

'I wanted to see your face when you saw the mosaics.' he cut her off abruptly. He pointed through the windscreen across the barren ground all round them towards a small town that hugged the brow of a hill on the horizon, its steeples and minarets poking up above the houses. 'That's Madaba,' he said.

CHAPTER V

The church looked quite ordinary on the outside. There was a concrete path that led up to the door which appeared at first to open on to a staircase and not into the church at all. Marion, already self-conscious in case Gregory should be disappointed by her reaction to the mosaics, turned an embarrassed face towards him and shrugged her shoulders. He pushed another door open beside her and smiled sardonically down at her. She felt completely witless and rather resented that he should have that effect on her.

She lowered her voice to a whisper. 'Are you sure this is the right place?'

'I've been here before,' he mocked her. He allowed the door to swing shut behind them and led her firmly up the main aisle of the church. The Christian guardian of the church came puffing along behind them, followed shortly afterwards by a sergeant in the tourist police.

'*Ahlan was-sahlan*,' the policeman said to Gregory. 'Welcome, madame.'

'*Ahlan bekum*,' Gregory murmured. He shook hands with both men, responding to their many questions about his welfare with evident pleasure. 'The policeman is a Moslem,' he said in an aside to Marion. 'The two men are forever arguing as to whether they can expect to see each other in Paradise.'

'It's true,' the policeman agreed, and smiled admiringly at her. He had the most perfect teeth Marion had ever seen, even in Jordan where nearly everyone seemed to have better teeth than most.

'I don't think anyone will be left out,' Marion smiled back at him. 'Not even we women.'

He laughed at that. 'It would not be Paradise without you,' he agreed lightly. 'Mr Gregory would want to come straight back to earth if that were so!' He

69

turned warm, teasing eyes on the man beside her. 'It's the first time he has brought a young lady with him here.'

Gregory turned away the implied question with a quick remark in Arabic. Marion would have loved to know what he had said, but nobody offered to translate for her benefit, and only the sly interest with which the guardian looked at her told her that it had been something about herself.

The mosaics weren't kept with any particular care. The guardian kicked aside the grubby coverings and handed a long wooden pointer to the policeman to help him give his exposition. He didn't hesitate to walk on the ancient map that was revealed to their gaze himself, and he was amused and showed it when Marion refused to follow his example.

Large portions of the map had been lost over the centuries. Some of it had fallen victim to the rebuilding of the church, some of it had been torn up to be used for something else. Only recently had the value of the mosaic been fully recognised not only because it was a thing of beauty in its own right, but because the Greek place-names had revealed the whereabouts of many places whose exact location had been long since forgotten.

The most famous portion was Herod's Jerusalem, complete with the seven city gates and maze of tiny streets all faithfully reflected. Above it was the River Jordan, optimistically filled with fish which have certainly never seen the light of day in its saline waters, which led into the Dead Sea. There were Bethany, and Bethlehem; Calvary and the Mount of Olives; the Sinai Desert and even Cairo straddling the River Nile.

'Does it come up to your expectations?' Gregory asked her.

She squatted down on an island of concrete and examined the chips of stone with care, noting how they had been placed in position, here to make the leaves of a palm-tree, there to form the letters of a place name.

'It's fantastic,' she said. 'I wish it were complete.' Her joy in it was written clearly on her face and she had forgotten that she had meant to draw a decent veil over her emotions when Gregory was anywhere on the horizon. She laughed up at him, her mobile features alight with sheer delight. 'Was it you who told my father about the mosaics here?'

'It may have been,' he admitted. 'It's earlier than the period I'm interested in, of course.'

She chuckled. 'It's too late to pretend that you haven't very catholic interests, Gregory Randall! Oh, thank you for bringing me here!'

His smile wasn't disapproving at all. 'I haven't finished with you yet,' he said drily. 'There are some very creditable floor mosaics in the museum, but we'll have a cup of tea first at the Rest House.'

'Isn't it a pity to go inside?' she objected.

'We can sit in the garden if you like, but the sun will feel hotter by the Dead Sea. It's always warm down there.'

But it seemed a shame to Marion to waste a moment of the sunshine. She was still at the stage of hoarding up the sunny hours as though there might not be any more on the morrow. It was warm now, but it was still winter and it had to rain sometimes, even in Jordan.

The man who ran the Rest House was plainly devout. He held his prayer-beads in one hand, feeding them through his fingers two at a time, even when he talked. He turned off the radio as soon as they came in, humming happily to himself.

'If you wait a few minutes I'll make you something to eat,' he almost pleaded with them. To have no more than a cup of tea was a slight on his hospitality. Surely they would wish to consume something more than that?

'I'd really like a fresh orange-juice,' Marion smiled at him.

71

The beads flashed through his fingers faster than ever. 'I will bring some *Kanafa* for you also,' he insisted.

Marion looked enquiringly at Gregory. 'It's a kind of cake, filled with white cheese and served with a hot syrup, and sometimes with nuts as well. It's a speciality of Nablus. Khazim came originally from there. It's delicious,' he added, nodding his consent to the man. 'You'll like it.'

Marion did, as she had liked all the food which had come her way in the last week. She found it pleasant, too, to sit on a crumbling wall in the garden of the Rest House and wonder about the mosaic floor at her feet that was beginning to break up in the open air.

'This is better than working,' she said to Gregory. In that moment she wasn't frightened of him at all. Indeed, his presence warmed her and made her feel at one with the whole world.

'Much better. Are you going to swim in the Dead Sea?'

She shook her head. 'I might paddle to find out what it's like.'

'Are you always so cautious?'

She laughed. 'I like to keep well within my depth,' she confessed. 'But I don't mind if you want to swim.'

'You can't sink in the Dead Sea,' he comforted her. 'I wouldn't let you drown in any circumstances, but you don't have to worry in water that's twenty-five per cent saline.'

She gave him a curious glance, wondering if it were only the Dead Sea he was talking about.

'It's easy for you to talk,' she said. 'It would have to be pretty deep for you to get out of your depth!'

'You might enjoy the excitement of coming out to my level?' he suggested, smiling.

But she was less than convinced. 'I'll think about it,' she offered.

'Do that,' he agreed. 'You may surprise yourself.'

She pondered about what he had meant by that all the time they were looking at the mosaics in the museum. The authorities had taken over three houses that, until quite recently, had had ordinary families living in them, and had done their best to preserve the delightful mosaics that they had inherited from their ancestors of many centuries before. One had to step down to get inside the houses. It was a reminder that Madaba was built on a hill that had been formed by previous townships that had gone before. It had been mentioned in the Book of Numbers, and who knew what its history had been before that?

She pondered, but she didn't come to any firm conclusion. Not even when they left the museum and went back to the car. Perhaps, she thought, he tried to make his mark with every girl he met, and most of them, she had no doubt, encouraged him with everything they had. If she had thought there was any future in it, she might have been tempted herself. But she knew her limitations. Men like Gregory Randall didn't, in her experience, interest themselves for long in girls who were five foot nothing in their stockinged feet, and the pain of parting would be all on her side, for her defences against him were already tumbling into dust, whereas he had hardly noticed the collision that had caused the damage. It was frightening to think a kiss could be no more than a kiss, or it could be a catalyst after which nothing would ever be quite the same.

He put his head very close to hers. ' *Shu fee*? ' he said in such warm, sympathetic tones that she was quite undone.

' What? What did you say? '

' What's the matter? You look as though you have the cares of the whole world on your shoulders.'

' Do I? I was thinking.' But she wasn't going to tell him what she had been thinking. ' I was wondering how my mother was getting along.'

' I don't think you need worry about her. She has

73

courage, and the ability to make the best of things wherever she is.'

Marion put her head on one side, conjuring up a mental picture of her mother. 'Why did you make her go and stay in your house in Devon?' she asked.

He looked amused. 'I thought the change would do her good. You were lucky in your parents, Marion Shirley.'

'Yes, wasn't I?' she said immediately. 'I'm glad you like her,' she added. Her eyes brimmed over with sudden mirth. 'She thinks you're dishy too!'

'And what does her daughter think?'

The laughter sobered into fright, a panic that whirled round her ears and left her feeling weak inside and not quite herself. 'I don't know you well enough to say,' she said.

'That's not what your mother told me?'

She turned questioning eyes to his. 'What did she say?'

'That you didn't like me,' he said shortly. 'Isn't that what you told her?'

'I told her you didn't like me. I couldn't remember anyone having disliked me before.' Oh dear, she thought, now he would think she was conceited as well. 'They may not have liked me much,' she hurried on, 'but they didn't actually dislike me, so that I could feel it when they looked at me. But I told her you were handsome too,' she ended up to sweeten the pill.

'People must have felt strongly about you before,' he remarked with a mildness that betrayed his lack of interest.

'Not like that!' Nobody had ever made her feel so aware of their presence in a room before that she would have known they were there if she had been struck both deaf and blind. 'Why don't you like me?' The words confused her by their stark brevity. It wasn't the kind of thing one asked, and now she knew why. Whatever he said could only add to the burden of pain she

74

had carried since first meeting him.

'Liking is too tame for you, too indifferent. You can't expect many men to like you until you're an old, old woman, my dear.'

Her eyes opened wide, her heart hammering against her ribs. 'I think that's a compliment,' she said. And then, when he didn't contradict her, 'I wish I were taller and as sophisticated as a dry Martini!'

His glance swept over her, raising her colour as she wished the words unsaid. 'I might *like* you then,' he agreed. 'If it's liking you really want?'

She shrugged her shoulders. 'What else?'

'From me?' He considered the matter. 'I could think of one or two things, but I don't think you're ready to hear about them.' He laughed suddenly. 'Some people think a taste for dry Martinis is rather old-fashioned nowadays,' he told her.

'Do you?' The words were out before she had thought what their impact might be. 'I mean—'

'Cocktails were never to my taste,' he answered her. 'I prefer the desert and the simple life.'

Yet he had found her too unsophisticated to bother with again after she had accused him of playing games with her. But then there was more than one meaning to the word "simple". It could mean that it wasn't capable of being analysed, and that meaning suited Gregory very well. She didn't think she'd ever get to the bottom of him if she were to stay in his castle all her life—

She took a quick intake of breath. 'Oh, look!' she said. 'Is *this* where Moses died?'

'It's where he's alleged to have made his last gesture towards the Promised Land,' he confirmed. He parked the Land Cruiser in the lee of a wall and came round to her side, lifting her bodily out into the boisterous wind. 'You'd better hang on to my hand,' he bade her. 'We don't want you to blow away!'

Moses' spirit had retained a violence that was enough

to flatten most of his visitors to the ground.

'Is it always like this?' Marion gasped.

'It always has been every time I've come here. Come and look over the edge and see if you think it was worth spending forty years in the wilderness to get there.'

The hills fell in folds down the valley below, which was green but which she doubted had ever been the rich pastureland that was implied in the description of a land flowing with milk and honey. Gregory pointed out Jerusalem and Jericho to her, and she was able to see the Dead Sea for herself, dominating the view, the lowest spot on earth, and the beginning of the great rift in the earth's surface that had buried Sodom and Gomorrah and which spread right down through East Africa to Malawi in the south.

'I always felt sorry for Moses,' she said, 'but I don't any longer. I'd be quite content to die in a place like this.'

'Away from England and the people you love best?'

'I'd find someone to love out here,' she declared, positive that it would be so.

'Could you?' he insisted. 'Wouldn't you pine at all?'

She shook her head. 'It's rather awful, isn't it? There must be all sorts of things I'd miss, but I feel quite at home here. It has a familiar feel. I can't explain any better than that!' The wind, tearing at her clothes, blew her words away and she was almost sure he hadn't heard her. It didn't matter. Why should he care whether she felt at home here or not?

'What about your mother?' he mouthed at her.

It was a shock that she hadn't considered her mother at all. 'I make a poor subsititute for my father. He was her whole life. She's bored as well as lonely without him.'

'That's what I thought,' he said.

Marion went a little nearer to the edge, meeting the

76

full force of the wind as she stepped out of Gregory's wake. She felt quite dizzy for a moment and when she felt his strong hands on her shoulders, anchoring her down, she was conscious only of relief that he was still there.

She turned her head and smiled at him. He looked as secure as the Rock of Gibraltar standing there and she found herself wishing that she had some right to his continued care. She could not recollect that she had ever wanted to lean on anyone else's strength before, not even her father who had had strong ideas about women being as independent as their brothers nowadays and who would have told her sternly that she had two quite adequate feet of her own to stand on. And so she had. She had received an education that had been every bit as good as it would have been if she had been the much desired son both her parents had wanted; and that, coupled with her own ability, meant that she was earning as much if not more than most of her contemporaries. But Gregory Randall could outdistance her in every field, and that was a novelty in itself.

'What is your Promised Land?' she asked him.

His answer was as unexpected as she had half known it would be. ''O my America! my new-found-land.' He looked amused. 'I'll settle for that.'

She had placed the quotation at once as coming from John Donne, but it seemed to her to be quite out of context. 'But he was talking about a woman,' she objected. And more intimately than most clerics would have done, she could have added.

'So was I,' Gregory told her.

'Oh!' she said, shocked, and then again, 'Oh!'

'You shouldn't jump to conclusions,' he rebuked her. 'You did say my *promised* land, not one I already had in my possession.'

He was being flippant, she knew, but she couldn't laugh it off as she would have done with anyone else.

77

What woman? Did he mean Denise? Or had he changed his mind about Judith? Or was it someone she had never heard of? Whoever it was, she hated her with a viciousness that was quite foreign to her usual sunny nature.

'I hope she's worth it,' she said out loud. She wriggled her shoulders under his hands. 'How do you know she won't bore you after a while?'

His fingers bit into her flesh. 'Never! I may wring her neck out of sheer exasperation, but I don't expect to be bored—'

She shook herself free and walked away from him, back to the safety of the wall of the terrace where Moses was supposed to have stood. 'I hope you won't be!' Her voice said she hoped he would be bored stiff, but she couldn't help that. 'She'll probably expect you to join the jet-set and won't be in the least bit interested in your books!'

He put his hands on his hips and he laughed at her, his face creasing into lines of amusement that made her crosser than ever.

'Well, if you don't like my Promised Land, what is yours?' he challenged her.

She had no answer ready for him. How could she have? It came into her mind that she had no ambitions for conquest in her own right. She wanted someone to take the trouble to conquer her, if conquest there had to be. She wanted to be *his* land, and to give up the riches within her to *him* in the mock battle of love. She stared at him with puzzled eyes.

'I'll never reach my Promised Land,' she said. 'I'm more like Moses than I knew. Did you know he stammered?' she added on a forlorn note. 'He was afraid people would laugh at him when he spoke to them, so God told him to take Aaron to speak for him.' She could have done with an Aaron now, someone with a golden voice, who could speak for her, hiding the discovery she had just made about herself from Gregory's

78

observant eyes. She simply could not bear it if he were ever to feel sorry for her!

'You should have more faith,' he told her. 'Do you want to see the old church over there, or shall we go on to the Dead Sea?'

She chose to go on. She was no longer in the mood for sightseeing. More than anything she wanted to go home and have time to bury her discovery so deeply within herself that it would never be found again. And going home meant going back to Gregory's castle. It never even crossed her mind that it could mean anywhere else. If she had, she would have despaired that she could be so irrational as to suppose that the best place to hide from Gregory was in his own private stronghold in the middle of the desert, the one place where she couldn't get away from him.

There were stones beside the road telling them when they had descended to sea level, a hundred metres below, two hundred, and lastly three hundred metres below the Mediterranean. A faint shimmer veiled the further bank, blurring the geographical features and the dark splodges that might have been merchant ships, loading and unloading their cargoes.

The waters of the Dead Sea were not as still as Marion had expected. Gregory drove into what looked like an amusement park which, abandoned for the most of the week, was full of people from Amman, making the most of the Moslem day of rest. Even so, the stony beach was emptier than it would have been anywhere in Europe, and there was plenty of room for Marion to kick off her shoes and walk along the edge of the warm water, marvelling that it should feel more like oil than water against her bare skin. The sun beat down on them, hotter than she would have believed possible, and after a while, the surrounding peace seeped into her troubled spirit and she felt quite content to allow events to take their own course without kicking too hard against the pricks. Denise was not yet installed in the Castle of the Cisterns, and nor was anyone else!

Marion began to look for pebbles that she thought would polish well. It had long been a hobby of her mother's, turning out polished stones as pieces of modern jewellery and selling them at local Oxfam bazaars and other such functions. There were several pebbles that she thought would come up well, some in a very pretty green colour and others of a marbled brown.

Gregory smiled down at her intent face as she searched, dipping her hands through the lazy, breaking waves that just covered her feet.

' For your mother? ' he asked.

She sat back on her heels. ' How did you know? ' she demanded.

' She told me she had made that barbaric necklace you were wearing at that evening class of yours.'

The beginnings of a frown appeared between her eyes. What a cosy gossip they must have had about her even to have discussed the details of what she had been wearing!

' Yes, she did,' she said.

Gregory spread himself full length on the pebbles and shut his eyes. ' If you didn't want it to be noticed you shouldn't wear it,' he pointed out reasonably enough.

It wasn't the necklace, it was what else he might have noticed that bothered her. She was beginning to think that nothing escaped those sharp eyes of his.

' It would look better on Denise— '

He came to life with a speed that rooted her to the spot. His long arms scooped her up from the edge of the water and deposited her beside him, high and dry on the beach.

' I told you what would happen if you mentioned her name this afternoon!' he threatened her. To her astonished ears he sounded as though he were very much enjoying himself. She struggled upwards into a sitting position and smoothed down her skirt with an agitated hand. 'Well?' he said.

'I'm going back to the car,' she muttered.

'Don't you like it here?' he teased her, his fingers brushing the white salt from the sea from the backs of her hands.

'I did, but you've spoilt it,' she said baldly. 'I don't like being pounced on!'

He sat up too and raised her hands to his lips, kissing them lightly before he released her completely.

'I'm sorry, love.' He stood up. 'Come on, I'll take you home.'

She was caught between relief and a sharp disappointment that he should take her at her word. She trailed after him back down the beach, hardly noticing the hard pebbles beneath her feet.

'Gregory,' she called after him, 'I was wrong. I didn't mean—'

He waited for her to catch up with him. 'But you don't trust me either, do you, Marion?'

Was it him or herself she didn't trust? She didn't know. But she didn't want to quarrel with him either. For some reason that hurt her to the quick.

'Please, Gregory,' she said, 'don't make things more difficult!'

He touched her cheek with a gentle hand, but the harshness stayed in his eyes as he looked down at her. 'You're making it difficult for yourself,' he told her. 'Real life isn't a dream, or a picture on a wall, my dear. You have to take the rough with the smooth, and sometimes it's the rough that makes the whole thing worthwhile in the end.'

'You mean that texture is as important as colour?' she hazarded.

He shrugged his shoulders. 'Something like that. You can spoil things for me too, more easily than you know. Men have their dreams too—'

Yes, someone like Denise! She already knew that! She put up her hand and caught his in hers, pulling it away from her face.

'Then you ought to know better than to make use of substitutes!' she lambasted him. 'It *never* works! Even I can tell you that!'

'Where on earth have you been?'

Marion hoped Gregory hadn't noticed the sulky note in Denise's voice. The French girl had worked herself into a fine rage and was looking very handsome as she faced her host across the width of the drawing-room.

'Does it matter?' Gregory returned the question. If Denise were wise, Marion thought with a shiver, she would drop the subject for tonight at least. Gregory was in no mood to be questioned by anyone about his movements or anything else. Marion was still smarting from his scathing comments on her well-meant attempt to tell him that she understood he was using her as an understudy for his real leading lady, but that she couldn't approve of his desire to rehearse what she felt was already a perfect performance.

'I thought you were going to *work*!' Denise went on, her voice raw and ugly. 'You deliberately tricked me into going to Jaresh with Gaston and Lucasta. You know I'd never have gone if I thought you—'

'I'm not interested,' Gregory cut her off.

Denise crossed the room at a run, throwing herself against his broad chest. Marion shut her eyes and tried to pretend that the searing pain within her was not jealousy because she would never have the courage to make such a move towards Gregory herself. She turned her back on them and walked slowly down the corridor towards her bedroom. Denise obviously knew how to handle her man. She wouldn't panic when he kissed her, but then she would know that it meant something between them, that it wasn't just a game that men and women play to pass the time until the right, the one and only, partner came along.

There was someone in her room. Marion paused at

the threshold, schooling herself to face Lucasta and to hear all about her day out with Gaston. But when she opened the door it was not Lucasta but Zein who was waiting for her, standing motionless in the middle of the floor. There was no indication as to how long she had been there, but she looked up and smiled when Marion came in, bursting into voluble speech and pointing towards the wall and the little *houri* Marion had spent the morning painstakingly cleaning.

Marion shook her head, trying to get across to the Bedu girl that she couldn't understand a word she was saying. Zein babbled happily on, leading Marion towards the dressing-table and the looking glass that stood on it. With a gesture of triumph she pointed towards Marion's reflection in the glass and then at the *houri* on the wall. Her excitement knew no bounds and, after a few moments, Marion understood why. No wonder the *houri* had had a familiar look to her. She could well have been a portrait of Marion herself!

CHAPTER VI

Lucasta was speaking. She was bored without Gaston's company and although she suspected that Marion was equally bored with hearing about him it was the only subject that interested her at the moment.

'Denise would have spoilt everything if she could. That was a dirty trick of that uncle of mine to send her off with us. Well, we've made jolly sure that it doesn't happen next week-end! Gregory is going to her place on the express invitation of her father. Gaston saw to that!'

Marion frowned at the wall in front of her. It was ridiculous to go to pieces just because he was going away. If she were going to live with herself at all, she would have to do better than that!

'But Gaston is coming here?' she managed to ask.

Lucasta half-closed her eyes, an expression of bliss on her face. 'I shall have him to myself for three whole days!'

Marion made a great effort and put her own problems to the back of her mind while she tried to face up to her responsibilities where her charge was concerned. If anyone had gone with Gaston and Lucasta to Jaresh the week-end before it should have been her. She ought to have made it her business to have found out a great deal more about this young French engineer, no matter what Gregory had said. She stopped what she was doing and turned round to face Lucasta.

'How much do you like this Gaston?' she asked her.

Lucasta was startled into opening her eyes wide. 'Very much. Well, not liking exactly.' She smiled up at Marion, looking very like her uncle. 'He sends me more than any man I've ever met! It's much more fun than I had supposed to be the object of someone's devotion. He's sweet!'

'Then it isn't serious?' Marion said with relief.

'Of course it's serious! Only I haven't made up my mind yet exactly how serious.'

This was worse than Marion had thought. 'It's very easy to confuse what is really a passing infatuation with the real thing,' she proffered hopefully.

Lucasta merely looked smug. 'Is that what happened to you when you were seventeen?'

'I don't remember,' Marion said firmly.

Lucasta laughed. 'Meaning that you're not telling me! I don't blame you, darling Marion. You have enough on your plate just now!' She eyed the elder girl with blatant curiosity. 'Is it infatuation with you?'

'What *are* you talking about?' Marion gasped, the cold, sinking feeling in her middle spreading down to her knees.

'I'm talking about Uncle Gregory,' Lucasta drawled. She stood up, looking for all the world like a little cat grown tired of playing with the toy of the moment. 'Oh, don't worry about it! I shouldn't think anyone else has noticed—certainly not the great man himself! —but you do go soft inside every time he comes on the scene, don't you? I recognise the signs. I feel exactly the same whenever I see Gaston.'

'I like your uncle—' Marion began. How extraordinary, she thought, that anyone's heartbeat should quicken over anyone as ordinary as Gaston Brieve.

'Oh, Marion!' Lucasta mocked her. 'Like? You're potty about him! You don't like him at all either. You're too far gone to *like* him, nothing so simple! Men do complicate things, don't they?' She sighed heavily. 'Still, it's nice to know that one doesn't have to be seventeen to make a fool of oneself. You're still at it at twenty-something and, if anything, you're more badly smitten than I am!'

'I am not!' Marion denied indignantly. 'And I do like your uncle. I like his books!'

'Do you?' Lucasta sounded impressed. 'Do you

know, I like hearing about Gaston's work too, and it's the most boring thing imaginable! He works out stresses and strains by mathematics, and horrible things like that! '

' I liked Gregory's books before I'd ever met him! ' Marion insisted with a blind disregard for the actual sequence of events. How terrible that she should lie about anything so stupid! ' Well, before I'd met him properly,' she amended.

' I know, one look was enough! '

' It wasn't, you know,' Marion contradicted her, feeling a little calmer. ' I disliked him excessively when I first saw him! '

' Good for you! ' Lucasta exclaimed. ' It must have been that that caught his interest because he doesn't usually bother with the *hoi-polloi*, any more than my mother does, only he's more polite about it. Not being rude, but you're not in the same class as our Denise, are you? '

' No.' It was a murmur of despair, but Lucasta showed no signs of recognising it as such.

' Actually,' she opined, ' you're much better looking than Denise, and whole streets nicer, but Daddy's money gives her a head start with Gregory. Well, I mean, who wouldn't be flattered to have their bird flying in every week-end without fail and hanging on his every word? '

' It must be more than that! She's very much in love with him—'

' Rubbish. Denise is incapable of loving anyone but herself, as anyone with half an eye could see. Only men never can add up where women are concerned. It excuses Gregory in a way. But if you can't see it, you must be a fool! '

Marion felt the time had come to protest. ' Lucasta, I will not be spoken to like that. Even if I am a fool, I'd rather you kept the fact to yourself! '

Lucasta gave her an exasperated look which included

86

a certain affection that she herself found surprising. Like the rest of her family, she did not suffer fools gladly.

'Meaning that you hadn't seen it,' she stated implacably. 'Do you deliberately go round in blinkers, or can't you help it?'

'Lucasta!'

'Oh, Marion, really! And you were all set to give me a nice little lecture on the dangers of being impressionable and giving way to an adolescent infatuation over Gaston. Did you really think it would do any good? At least I see Gaston as he is, warts and all! I'm much less likely to get hurt than you are. You make me feel positively *old*!'

'Lucasta, I don't!'

'Old,' Lucasta repeated with ruthless candour. 'If you want Gregory you'll have to do more than spend your time washing down his walls. Why don't you stun him by staging some dramatic coup?'

Marion's sense of humour got the better of her and she smiled, her whole face lighting up with laughter. 'Are you mad?' she demanded. 'Gregory wouldn't turn a hair if I sat down at his table stark naked!'

Lucasta giggled. 'He's not easily thrown,' she agreed. 'You'd be far more embarrassed than he.'

'Exactly!' Marion said. 'So I think I'll go on washing down his walls and leave the field clear for Denise.'

'Pity,' said Lucasta. 'I'd prefer having you in the family. Tell you what, I'll ask Gaston to bring somebody down for you this week-end with him. He says there are lots of spare males hanging round the site where he works.'

'Thanks very much!' Marion raised her eyebrows, trying to look stern, but the legacy of laughter still lingered in her eyes. 'I shall be working this week-end. As it is, I'm never going to finish even these frescoes, let alone the main ones. It takes much longer than I had supposed.'

'You can't work all the time. You're meant to amuse me too and, frankly, if Gaston and I have to have someone around, and at the moment that's the way I want it, until I'm quite, quite sure that I want to take the next step with him, I'd much rather it were you than anyone else.'

Marion tried not to smile. 'I suppose I'm easily managed,' she put in. 'I may surprise you yet!'

'At least you won't die of shock if you catch us kissing one another,' Lucasta said frankly. 'To hear Denise talk you'd think the end of the world had come.'

Marion began to look anxious again. 'It depends on the circumstances. I think most people in a Moslem country are more circumspect than we are at home. It wouldn't do to upset them.'

'Right,' said Lucasta. 'That's exactly what Gregory said.' She made her voice sound passably like her uncle's. 'Do what you like, as long as you don't live to regret it, but don't shock the natives while you're doing it.' She smiled suddenly. 'Poor Marion, you do like to worry about nothing, don't you? Gregory trusts me to behave myself, and I'd do anything sooner than lose his respect, so you really don't have to worry about me. You'd better try trusting me too.'

'I do!' Marion claimed, much too quickly. 'It's only that you might not be able to help yourself.'

'Dear Marion, that's why I want you to come with us this week-end.' She looked at her, her eyes half-closed and considering. 'Of the two of us, I'd say you were the more likely to lose your head—which is another reason for sticking close to me!'

'But he'll be away—'

Lucasta slapped her thighs with glee. 'I knew it!' she exulted. 'You have fallen for him, haven't you? And if you won't do anything about it, I will!'

'No, no, you're not to. There's nothing you can do. Your uncle would be furious if you were to interfere—

and I would be too! I mean it, Lucasta! '

But the girl only laughed. ' Don't flap, darling, I was only teasing you! But you will come with us this week-end, won't you? '

Marion's panic that her young charge might call her uncle's attention to her when she was already afraid that he saw far too much subsided a little, leaving her feeling more than a little foolish.

' Where are we going? '

Lucasta shrugged. ' Gaston didn't say. He hates staying in one place, though. He's determined that I shall take a proper interest in my surroundings and gives me long lectures on the significance of a few dull little stones in the middle of nowhere whenever I let him. He's really very sweet! And very easy to distract, I'm thankful to say! '

Marion, growing used to Lucasta's exaggerated speech, wondered if it would be selfish to suggest that they should go to Petra. It still stung that Gregory should have refused to take her. It was the way he had done it, just as if he couldn't bear her company for two whole days. And she wouldn't have imposed on him, she would have been as quiet as a mouse, but it hadn't made any difference. Even if she had asked him, he had said he wouldn't take her.

' Let's go to Petra,' she said out loud. ' Next week-end. Oh, do let's, Lucasta! '

' Petra? Would Gaston like it? '

' I'm sure he would. It's a city carved out of rock. You must have seen pictures of it! '

Lucasta remained irritatingly unconvinced. ' But what would we do there? Gaston likes to get off by himself,' she added demurely, fluttering her eyelashes.

' It's a big place,' Marion told her. ' I believe it's at least ten square miles inside. There's only one place where you can get in to it through the hills. It's a tiny little passage, cut by an old river. It *must* be interesting from an engineering point of view! Couldn't you persuade him that you want to see it?'

'I could,' said Lucasta, 'but I'm not sure I want to. I'll think about it. I'm sorry to be maddening, but I may have made up my mind about Gaston by then and I'd rather keep our plans fluid.'

Marion returned to her work, trying to hang on to the shreds of her good temper. 'All right, think about it! But whatever you decide you're not going off alone with Gaston—not with Gregory away and only me to keep an eye on you, whether I trust you or not!'

'I'll think about it,' Lucasta repeated. She watched Marion work for a few minutes and then said maliciously, 'Zein told Gregory she had seen your picture on the wall. She wanted to know what you were doing there. And do you know what she told him? She said you were waiting for him!'

Marion's eyes flew to the little *houri*. He had said more or less the same thing to her, she remembered, only she hadn't seen the likeness between herself and the painted figure then. And, of course, he had been joking! She had laughed then, but she couldn't find it in her heart to laugh now. Now, she couldn't see anything funny about it at all.

'There's a letter for you. Will you come and collect it after dinner?'

Marion nodded. She had only addressed two words directly to Gregory all week and she wondered now why he couldn't have brought her letter with him to the table. If she went into his study she would have to say something, and she had nothing to say to him.

She knew he was watching her all the time they were eating, but she refused to look back at him. If she did, she might betray herself, and he would know that she ached to ask him to come and look at the frescoes, even more to ask him if he was really going to stay with Denise this coming week-end. Sooner or later, she was going to have to speak to him about the frescoes. No matter how hard she worked, she couldn't possibly finish even the ones in her bedroom in the few weeks of this holiday. She would need months rather than weeks to complete her task.

It was the first time she had been in his study. It was a comfortable room, with a strongly Eastern emphasis in the furnishings. Marion knew that the Arabic for office was *diwan*, the same word in effect as divan, where the great man would once have lounged as he directed his minions to carry out his day-to-day business. There was a divan here too, a day-bed with an elaborately carved wooden back that looked beautiful but not very comfortable. There were some leather pouffes dotted around too, and a screen between the huge desk and the door which had some of the loveliest fretwork Marion had ever seen. It was the ikons on the wall that claimed her immediate attention, however. They were dark with age, glinting gold in the lamplight, and she knew as soon as she saw them madly valuable.

'They must have been what you wrote to my father about!' she exclaimed, moving in closer to see them better. 'Oh, how he must have envied you such a fine collection!'

Gregory sat down in the chair behind the desk. 'Don't you want your letter?'

'Oh yes, of course.' She didn't even pause in her examination of the ikons. There was one particularly beautiful one of Cosmos and Damian that took her breath away. She could have done with hours to look at that one alone. 'Did my father ever see these?'

'He bought some of them for me in the London sales.'

'I'm surprised he could bear to let them out of his sight,' she gloated. 'How did you persuade him?'

'He didn't seem to be a particularly envious man,' Gregory remarked.

'No, he wasn't. Far from it. But these ikons are

91

something else, aren't they?' She studied one of the larger ones which was carved in an arch and from which most of the paint had fallen. It had probably once been the lid of a monk's chest in which he had kept the few personal possessions allowed to him. Beneath the paint, the wood was grey with age.

'Yes, they're something else,' Gregory agreed. 'They've taught me something too, something I think your father always knew. You can't own things of beauty; the most you can do is to look after them for a while. Ownership is a very relative term.'

She was surprised that he had known her father so well when at most they could have exchanged a few letters.

'My father always said it was a privilege to see great works of art,' she confided. 'He used to say that the effect they had on oneself was the only part of them one could possess. He could look at things much more objectively than I can, though. With me it's a mood thing. I need to see something in every kind of mood before I know it. I'm only just getting to know the frescoes in my room.'

He smiled across the room at her. 'I'd say you were more appreciative than most.'

She smiled back, forgetting her nervousness of him. 'I'd be pretty dull of mind if I didn't like them a little, my father being the man he was.' She advanced across the room, her eyes alight. 'May I come back some time and look at them again? I wouldn't interrupt you while you were working, but while you're away at the week-end, for instance. Please, may I?'

'Who told you I'd be away for the week-end?'

'Lucasta.' She sat down on one of the pouffes, tucking her feet up under her. It was nice in here, she thought, alone with Gregory and with his ikons all about them. She wouldn't spoil it by dwelling on his chosen companion for the week-end because she would spoil it all.

He watched her settling herself with a slight smile. 'Does it take you as long to get to know people?' he asked her. 'Do you have to see them in every mood too?'

She had never thought about it. 'I suppose people are more complicated,' she answered. 'They have different moods too. It isn't the same because everything they say changes what I feel all the time. Pictures are less demanding in the long run.'

'They don't cut up your peace like people do?'

Her sober expression broke into laughter. 'Sometimes. Nobody ever did before—' She broke off, giving him an apologetic look. 'Peace isn't *everything*!' she added by way of offering him an olive branch.

'No. I prefer to be challenged myself.' He held out her letter to her and she took it from him, meaning to read it later. 'I think you may find it more exhilarating too when you get used to it.'

She felt shy under the probing of his navy-blue eyes and turned her letter over in her hands. 'Oh, good! It's from Mother. I wonder how she's enjoying Devon.'

'Why don't you open it and find out?'

Her fingers shook a little as she pulled the closely written pages out of the envelope. She didn't want his eyes on her when she read it. He would know as if he had read it himself what was in it. He would know that she hadn't wanted her mother to stay in his house in Devon—*and he would know why*!

She allowed her eyes to slide over the lines of her mother's writing and stiffened, unable to believe what she was reading.

'What is it?' Gregory asked, amused.

'My mother likes Devon,' she told him in cool, stilted tones. 'She's sleeping better than she was in London and she likes having something to do.'

There were little lights in his eyes reflected from the lamp in front of him. When she looked up at him, she found them quite hypnotic and it took a distinct effort of will to look away again.

'Your mother likes a challenge too,' he told her.
'You're more like her than you allow.'

She read a little further and her whole world fell in
on top of her. 'She wants to move to Devon for good! '
she whispered. 'She wants to sell the house in London. But you can't want her in your house for ever? '
She looked down at the floor. 'And what am I to do? '

'What do you want to do? ' His voice was bracing
and she managed a quavery smile because she didn't
want him to think that she lacked spirit, though she
must do because she felt quite flattened by the news.

'I like the school where I teach. They're expecting
me back next term. I have to give them some notice if
I'm going to leave.'

She consulted the letter, struggling to move the lump
in her throat before it reached astronomical proportions. She swallowed hard as the words blurred before
her eyes.

'She thinks I can get a job in Exeter.' She laughed
shortly. 'It's only *twenty miles* away! It's years since
we had a car and we couldn't possibly afford to run
one and, even if we could, *I* can't live in your house
too! ' She looked up at him, an unconscious appeal in
her eyes. 'She must be mad to think you'd want either
of us there on a permanent basis! '

He was silent for a long moment, then he said, 'It's
a nice house. I think you'd like it.'

'But—'

'It suits me very well to have your mother living
there. I was hoping she would want to stay on. I'm
there very seldom, but the house has been in our family
for a good many generations and I like to know it's
there to go back to whenever I want to. We had some
marvellous holidays there as children.'

The appeal in her eyes changed to accusation. 'You
meant her to make her home there? '

'I did suggest that she might think about it,' he ad-
94

mitted. 'Your father's ghost was making the London house unbearable to her.' He bent forward until his head was on the same level as hers. 'Do you really mind so much?'

She nodded. 'Even if I paid you an economic rent I'd feel I'd lost my independence. I'd have nothing to offer in return.'

'Isn't that for me to decide?' He sat back, his face in shadow, and Marion felt a shiver inside her at his change of mood. 'I was going to speak to you about next term in any case. How are the frescoes going?'

'I've hardly begun.'

He glanced at her and she couldn't begin to tell what he was thinking. 'As a job, how does it compare with teaching?'

'There is no comparison,' she returned. 'Teaching is bread and butter and what I do to earn my living; the other is ambrosia. It's the most marvellous opportunity I've ever had to do the kind of thing I really want to.'

'Then you'd better stay here until you've finished the job,' he said drily.

'*I can't*!'

Her passionate refusal hadn't put him out one jot. 'Why not?' His very calmness made her feel the more distraught.

'Why not?' she repeated. 'It should be obvious to anyone why I can't stay here! When Lucasta goes back to England—'

'Good heavens, aren't there enough other females around to suit the proprieties?' he exploded.

She shivered. 'Only Denise,' she murmured. 'And she's only here at week-ends.'

The dislike he felt for her was naked in his eyes and the lump came back into her throat, making her feel more miserable than ever. She already knew he thought her prudish and over-concerned about Lucasta, but she couldn't bring herself to say that she would stay on in

95

his castle alone with him. It might not matter to him, but for her it would be total disaster. She couldn't go on pretending for ever, and she was almost sure she wouldn't want to, and she would be the one to be hurt —more than she was now, if that was possible!

'There's Zein and Umm Hanim, or don't they count in your scheme of things?' he asked her nastily.

But she knew without being told whose side they would be on. 'Perhaps Denise wouldn't mind staying for a while—if her father can spare her—'

'I think not,' he said with unexpected firmness. 'I'll write to your mother and see what she suggests. She can give in your notice at the same time to that school of yours, which should give them nearly a fortnight to find a replacement.' He moved and the light fell squarely on his face and his eyelashes seemed all of an inch long. 'I thought you got on all right with the Bedouin women? You don't seem to share Denise's dislike for them?

'I do! I like them very much!' She wished he wouldn't stare at her like that. In fact she wished he wouldn't look at her at all.

'Then what's the matter?'

The gentleness of the question took her unawares and she blurted out the truth before she could help herself.

'They'd think you'd kept me here for yourself. They wouldn't understand that there's nothing like that between us. They wouldn't think we could be—friends, or employer and employee, or anything like that.'

He raised his eyebrows with a touch of humour and the planes of his face were unbelievably handsome in the lamplight.

'Perhaps they're right.'

The words lay between them for a long moment and then she laughed. It was a reflex action, for she could see nothing funny in what he had said.

'But we're not—'

96

'We're not friends either, Marion.'

Her eyes fell before his. 'You said you'd try to be friends with me,' she reminded me.

'I must have been mad!' He came round the side of the desk and drew her to her feet. 'Shall I stay home this week-end?'

She took fright immediately. 'No. Gaston and Lucasta may take me to Petra.'

'You can go some other time,' he tempted.

But she shook her head. 'I want to go. I've always wanted to go to Petra!'

The corners of his mouth kicked up into a smile. 'I'm glad your mother is going to live in my house,' he said slowly. 'It makes our adoption of one another more official. Shall we celebrate our new relationship, you and I?'

His hands burned through he dress as he pulled her up on to the leather pouffe she had been sitting on. She blinked up at him.

'What relationship?'

He laughed, touching his lips to her brow. 'Kissing kin?' he suggested.

She could have escaped him if she had really wanted to do so. At no time did he coerce her to stand as still as a statue before him, nor did he force her to cling to him, afraid as she was that she might fall if she let go her hold on him.

'I'm not kin,' she said in a voice that sounded like someone else's and not even remotely like her own. 'I'm not kith either!'

'Just as I'm not your friend,' he confirmed. 'Nor do I want to be!'

He kissed her mouth and it was as if she had never been kissed before. Her heart seemed to have stopped within her and then, in a mad race to make up time, it rushed into a new rhythm that left her breathless with a dizzy happiness that he must have felt too, for he kissed her again with increasing passion, and then

97

put her away from him with a determination that chased the happy feeling away and left her feeling as insecure and awkward as ever.

He had remembered Denise, she thought, and shut her eyes in case he should see how much he had hurt her.

'I'm still going to Petra!' She clenched her fists. 'And I'm not staying here—not even to finish the frescoes!'

He brushed a tear from her cheek and smiled down at her. 'I'll keep you here somehow,' he said. 'If I don't restore the frescoes, I'll lose my tenancy of the castle.' His smile grew wider. 'I'll write to your mother tonight.'

'But—' she began. 'But nothing's decided, is it?'

'Isn't it?'

She put an agitated hand up to her mouth. 'You don't have to kiss me to get your own way! You can't make me—'

'Nobody's going to make you do anything you don't want to do,' he soothed her. 'Won't you trust me thus far?'

She didn't trust him at all, but then neither did she know what she wanted at the moment, other than to be held tight by him again. A fine fool he must think her to be in such a dither about nothing!

'I'll write to my mother too,' she said, not quite sure whether this was meant to be a threat or a promise. 'I'll go and write to her now!'

CHAPTER VII

'Well, that was a funny thing,' said Lucasta.

'What was?'

'Gregory says that Gaston must bring Jean-Pierre down on Thursday night with him so that he can vet him before he flies off with Denise on Saturday.'

'Vet Jean-Pierre?' Marion echoed. 'Whatever for?'

'That's what I'd like to know. What went on between you and Gregory last night? I hope you noticed how heavily tactful I was, keeping out of your way whil you spent *hours* with him in that study of his?'

Marion hadn't noticed. Indeed, she hadn't given Lucasta a thought at the time. She had been far too busy trying to control the turmoil within her that Gregory's kiss had let loose before it overwhelmed her carefully.
completely.

'He let me look at his ikons,' Marion explained

Lucasta grinned at her. 'His ikons or his etchings?'

Marion refused to be drawn. 'What time is Gaston coming?' she asked instead. 'In the middle of the night again?'

Lucasta was immediately on the defensive. 'Well, no one is asking you to wait up for him! He can introduce Jean-Pierre to you at lunchtime on Friday, and you're forbidden to do a stroke of work after that until first thing on Monday morning!'

'We'll see,' said Marion.

'No, we won't! It was kind of Gaston to bring Jean-Pierre with him, not that it was difficult to persuade him to come. I gave him your photograhg to show around and the volunteers came flocking round. You know, Marion, you're really very pretty! I hadn't noticed at school. I just thought you were nicer than any of the other hens who try to burden our minds with useless knowledge.' She chuckled at the expression on Marion's face. 'It was Gregory who pointed it out to me,' she added mendaciously. 'He said you had a face as revealing as a child in a candy store.'

'I have not!' Marion protested. 'And I'll thank you not to refer to your long-suffering teachers as hens. Have you no respect?'

'Hen is a term of affection. Hen, henny, hinny, honey, they all came originally from the Border Country, or so Miss Blandish says, and she ought to know, because she was probably alive at the time.'

Marion strove to keep a straight face. She, too, had been treated to some of Miss Blandish's eye-witness accounts of various events in history. 'Miss Blandish can't help being a little over-enthusiastic.'

Lucasta shrugged. She looked more curiously at Marion. 'Gregory was right,' she said faintly. 'You do shine like a lamp when you smile. Like a good deed in a naughty world, he said. He was rather impressed when I told him he was quoting from Shakespeare. He asked me if I was sure, and of course I wasn't, so he told me it came from *The Merchant of Venice*. Did you know that?'

'Well, yes, I did,' Marion admitted. '" *How far that little candle throws his beams! So shines a good deed in a naughty world* ".'

'Gosh!' said Lucasta. 'Do you think he meant it as a compliment?'

'No, I don't.' Marion had remembered how the scene went on. '*When the moon shone, we did not see the candle.*' Nor did he see her when Denise was by. It was the perfect simile, she thought ruefully. She felt every bit as sad and forlorn as a candle whose flame had been snuffed out by some careless hand—Gregory's hand! 'I always smile at the wrong moment,' she confessed ruefully. 'Your uncle prefers a more sophisticated approach.'

Lucasta nodded thoughtfully. 'Judith is as sophisticated as they come and very, very sure of herself. She leaves Denise standing! But I don't think Gregory *liked* her at all. He amused himself wearing her like a carnation in his buttonhole, and he probably found it fun to ruffle her perfect hair-do every now and then, but mostly he looked contemptuous whenever she appeared on the scene.'

It was quite a picture and Marion could see it as clearly as if she had been there. 'He isn't contemptuous of Denise,' she said. She hoped she didn't sound as jealous of the French girl as she felt.

'I don't know about Denise. It's just possible that Papa is the real attraction there. Papa Dain has only two loves in his life: darling Denise and his art collection. He makes money like some people win at Monopoly when they have all the right properties, but it's all spent on acquiring more and more *objets d'art*, with Denise as prime exhibit—indeed the only exhibit, for he buries all his other treasures in burglar-proof vaults under his house and only allows the favoured few in to look at them.'

'And Gregory is one of the favoured few,' Marion said unnecessarily. Of course he was! Denise would see to that!

Lucasta put on a worldly-wise expression and sighed deeply. 'He's all lined up to be the next exhibit, if you ask me. He's the most beautiful thing ever to have come Denise's way. He's a handsome devil when he wants to be!'

Marion made a face. 'He's too tall for me!' she joked.

But Lucasta didn't laugh as she had thought she would. 'If he wanted you,' she said, 'he wouldn't let a little thing like that stand in his way.'

Jean-Pierre was an apparently pleasant young man, with smiling eyes, and a willingness to be pleased by any member of the opposite sex who happened to come his way.

'*Comme tu es belle!*' he breathed over Marion's hand when he was duly introduced to her.

Marion frowned at him, very much on her dignity. 'Thank you,' she said in freezing tones.

'*Formidable!*' he murmured. 'When do we start for Petra?' He smiled at Marion, a glint in his eyes that she didn't quite like. 'Will you climb up to the High Place wth me? I shall be very nice to you!'

'What's up there?' she asked cautiously.

His eyes snapped. 'No people!'

'The Nabateans, who came up from Saudi Arabia bit by bit and replaced the Edomites at Petra, worshipped their god Dusares up there. They probably adopted him from the Edomites as well as their country. His name means "He (Lord) of Shera." Shera is the same word as Seir, by which name the district was known in the Old Testament. Jehovah, or Jahweh, the god of the Hebrews, was also said to be He of Seir, and to inhabit a rock called Beth El, the House of God. Dusares was symbolised by a block of stone, so they may have started out as the same person,' Gregory told her.

'But why a rock?' she asked.

'The Israelites weren't particularly artistic, and the same was true of the people on the "other side of the Jordan" as well. Besides, they were trying to get away from the Egyptian brilliance in this field which to them symbolised the oppression and the false gods they had escaped with such difficulty. A block of stone was far more acceptable as it represented the likeness of nothing in heaven above or on the earth beneath. The Nabateans, who were artistic, probably inherited the taboo as they inherited so much else from the Edomites.'

'But the Hebrew god—'

'It took time for God to reveal Himself to mankind,' Gregory said sardonically. 'The rock idea lingered for quite a while. "*The Lord is my rock, and my fortress, and my deliverer; The God of my rock; in him will I trust.*" Haven't you heard that before? And when Mohammed entered Mecca in triumph he found the temple there surrounded by three hundred and sixty idols in the form of blocks of stone and pillars, which he overthrew. It wasn't by chance that the three great monotheistic religions came from the Semitic people. They too had the same beginnings, not only their gods. They are all the sons of Abraham: some through Isaac, the son of Sara; and some through Ishmael, the son of Hagar.'

'I suppose so,' she said. She saw the bored look on Jean-Pierre's face and her conscience smote her. It had been nice of him to come and and she had done nothing so far to entertain him. She set herself to draw him out for the rest of the meal, asking about his work and his family, and making herself take an interest in his replies.

But she scarcely heard a word he said. With Gregory there, no other man seemed quite real to her. Would it be like that for the rest of her life? She could shut her eyes and see him as clearly as she could with them open. She could see the way his dark hair curled into his neck; the stern line to his mouth; the hardness of the line of his jaw; and, most of all, his observant navy-blue eyes that she sometimes thought could look right inside her and read her thoughts as easily as she could herself.

She must have made a better job of looking as though she was drinking in every word Jean-Pierre said than she had thought, because there was no getting rid of him after lunch. He followed her round the castle, never moving more than a few yards away from her, and at every turn Gregory seemed to be there, watching them with a superior amusement until Marion could have slapped him—and Jean-Pierre too for making her feel such a fool.

103

There was no sign of Gaston and Lucasta anywhere. If they had been going out, Marion wished they had taken Jean-Pierre and her with them. Anything would have been better than the awfulness of trying to make him drink tea like a civilised person in the drawing-room, a habit which he considered barbaric and English, especially when he had quite another entertainment in view.

'You wanted me to come, no?' he whispered in her ear. 'You *asked* for me to come?'

'Only because I didn't want to play gooseberry by myself!' she retorted.

'Play gooseberry? What is that?'

She explained the term. 'Lucasta is only seventeen and it's my job to look after her,' she finished somewhat primly.

'But you are not seventeen! You were never meant to be a gooseberry, *ma petite* Marion. You were meant for much better things than that. Lucasta, she is well enough for Gaston, but you are far too pretty for anyone else but me!'

'Jean-Pierre, I—'

'You are shy, a little, no? But no one is shy of me for long. A few kisses, *ma mie*, and you will forget all about your shyness.'

He would have suited the action to the words, but Marion excused herself hurriedly and rushed out of the room. She stood in the darkened hall of the frescoes, trying to catch her breath and wondering what to do next, when she heard Gregory talking to Abou Hanim outside. The Bedu had his transistor radio by his side and the sounds of one of the famous Umm Kalthoum's endless songs came clearly to her. She peeped out through one of the shuttered windows and saw the two men squatting in the dust, side by side, listening intently to the recorded voice of that most loved Middle Eastern singer. It was as if a spell had been cast on them by this latter-day idol from Egypt.

Marion smiled to herself. Seeing the effect Umm Kalthoum had on her audience, she had no difficulty in believing that the British had rated it of first importance to guard this extraordinary siren during the war, in case she should fall into Rommel's hands and be used by the German propaganda machine. She could bend and sway the emotions of men for hours at a time, as one of her songs, "You are My Life" (*Anta Umri*) which lasts for one hundred and sixty minutes, in its own right bears witness.

If Gregory was going to hear her out, she could safely take refuge in his study until Jean-Pierre tired of waiting for her and thought of something else to do. Gregory couldn't possibly have minded her going into the room where he worked, but it still felt like trespassing to Marion as she opened the door and slid inside. She turned her eyes away from the pages of the book he was writing on his desk and filled in time going from one to another of the ikons on the wall, studying them in detail while there was no one there to watch her.

After a while she forgot Jean-Pierre, and forgot that Gregory might come in and surprise her at any moment, so she nearly jumped out of her skin when his voice said from the doorway:

'I thought you might be here.'

She coloured guiltily. 'Has Jean-Pierre been looking for me?'

Gregory leaned against the jamb of the door, crossing his arms in front of him. 'Didn't you want him to?'

'I hoped he might have a look round by himself,' she confessed. 'If I'd stayed around much longer I'd have poured his tea all over him!'

Gregory smiled. 'You shouldn't have been so oncoming at lunch. I'm afraid he took that melting look of yours at face value.'

'Oh no!'

He laughed at her appalled expression. 'Weren't you

thinking of him at all? I rather thought not.'

She smiled back at him. ' How did you know? '

' You can't hide much from me, Marion Shirley. You hadn't turned the light on.' He laughed again.

' But it would be dreadful if he guessed! ' she protested. ' Only I'd much rather get on with the frescoes than entertain him. Is that awful of me? '

' Terrible! Are you asking me to rescue you from the clutches of that young man this week-end? '

' I expect I can cope with him,' she retorted. ' Anyway, I don't see what you could do. You can hardly ask him to go away, can you? '

He didn't look as though he rated her chances of coping with anyone to be above even. ' I'd be a little more subtle than that,' he said.

She edged towards the door before he could cast any more aspersions on her *savoir faire*. ' I'll manage,' she determined grimly. ' I have had followers before,' she added just in case he had doubted it. ' I'm quite a bit older than Lucasta and—'

' As pretty as a picture! ' he finished for her.

She ignored that, although she was glad that he thought so. ' Yes, well, you don't have to look after me. I've looked after myself for a long time now and I've never come to any harm.'

' Somehow,' he said drily, ' I doubt your defences have been much tested in the past.'

Only by him! She stood before him, a still, dignified little figure, her face completely serious. ' Jean-Pierre's ammunition isn't of a very high calibre.'

' High enough to make a nuisance of himself! ' Gregory crossed the room and flung himself into the chair behind the desk. ' I'm not prepared to take the risk,' he pronounced. ' I'm not leaving you on your own with that young cub on the prowl, and that's that.'

' But it isn't any of your business,' Marion pointed out. ' I'd rather you left things alone! ' She began to feel uncomfortable under his steady regard. ' You don't even like me! You said so! '

'You manage to amuse me more than most,' he said, beginning to laugh.

She glowered at him. It was not the emotion she would have chosen to inspire in his breast. 'I know that! '

He raised his eyebrows, his eyes holding a merciless gleam that was very disturbing to her. ' If you're going to stay, why don't you sit down? ' he asked.

But she was in no mood to settle anywhere. She knew she ought to go back to the drawing-room and Jean-Pierre, but she couldn't bring herself to go. She bit her lip, whipping up her independent spirit from the withered, craven stance that it wanted to adopt in his presence.

' Why don't you come to Beirut with me? ' he shot at her.

Oh, Denise would love that! Marion had no difficulty in imagining the French girl's reaction to an additional passenger, and a female one at that, when she thought she was going to have Gregory all to herself.

' I can't! I can't leave Gaston and Lucasta alone together. Besides, they're only going to Petra because I want to go. Gaston's booked a couple of rooms at the Rest House for tomorrow night. I have to go now! '

Gregory considered her thoughtfully. ' I don't like the sound of it,' he said. 'Never mind, don't you worry about it. I'll have a word with both Gaston and Jean-Pierre.'

His gesture was dismissive, but still she lingered. ' It isn't Jean-Pierre's fault,' she said after a while.

' I'm well aware of that! '

' He may want to go to Petra as much as I do,' she reasoned.

' I doubt it.' He put his hands behind his head and looked at her thoughtfully. ' Forget it, Marion, and sit down! Abou Hanim says Zein has taken to wearing lipstick—yours, I suppose? '

107

She nodded. 'I hope it didn't get her into any trouble?'

'Not with her husband. He thinks it's fine! But Basma, Umm Hanim, is rigid with disapproval. It isn't always easy to be the older and less attractive wife. Couldn't you give her a lipstick too?'

Marion peeped at him through her lashes. 'If I do, you'll have to bring me back a replacement from Beirut. I only have a couple left.'

His own eyes narrowed. 'What colour?'

'Something like the one I've got on,' she murmured.

He stood up slowly, moving closer to the window and beckoning to her to join him. 'I can't see it if you will stand over there in the shadows. Come a bit nearer and let me see.'

But she took fright. 'Any colour will do,' she assured him.

He beckoned again and she found herself going to him like metal to a magnet. He put his fingers under her chin and raised her face to his. 'Very pretty,' he commented. 'You may be small, but your proportions must be nearly perfect, yet you're not a vain person, are you?'

There was no answer to that. She pulled away from him, unable to bear his touch a moment longer. 'I can't help being small,' she said. 'It has all sorts of disadvantages.'

'Does it?' His eyes flickered over her and he smiled. 'It has its attractions too. Can I trust you to share your room with Lucasta on this expedition to Petra? She and Gaston may well try to talk you into some other arrangement.' He saw her outraged expression and laughed at her, giving her an affectionate pat on the behind. 'Oh, Marion, what a delight you are! As if you would permit Lucasta out of your sight while she's in your care! But, like Bo-Peep's sheep, you don't have to worry about that niece of mine. Leave her alone, and she'll come home, bringing young Gaston behind

108

her. Forget all about her and see all you can of Petra while you're there! '

And he bent his head and kissed her gently where the dimple came and went in her cheek. 'You'll like Petra,' he said. 'But look after yourself! '

'Well, well,' Lucasta murmured, 'now we see him, now we don't! What did you do to him, Marion? '

Marion looked blank. She had been as surprised as anyone when Jean-Pierre had marched across to Denise's tiny Piper and had swung himself on board. She thought she had been in the Frenchman's pocket every waking moment since she had wrested herself away from Gregory's study and the dangerous delight of his undivided attention on herself.

'I didn't do anything,' she denied.

'No,' said Gaston, 'she did not. He told me he would be leaving today. Some of the people who are going to be at Denise's party are friends of his people in France. They have daughters—' He cast an apologetic look at Marion. 'His family approve of them, you understand? Jean-Pierre's family are like that. It is an old family, and most of the old families of France only know each other.'

'And Marion isn't suitable? ' Lucasta demanded, bristling with indignation.

Gaston shrugged. 'There is no title,' he said simply.

Lucasta looked really angry. 'There's no title in my family either,' she informed him. 'Perhaps I should have told you sooner! '

Gaston gave her a quick hug, smoothing the cross lines from her face with his lips. 'It means nothing, *ma mie*. There is no title in my family either. But Jean-Pierre's family is very different. Even the Napoleonic titles are too *nouveaux* for them. It is not his fault.'

'Oh, isn't it? Well, he may be an aristocrat, but I don't think much of his manners! ' Lucasta rounded on him. 'I had no idea the French are like that!'

'They're not,' Marion put in peaceably. 'Your uncle thought it better it Jean-Pierre went to Beirut—'

'*What?*'

Marion wished she had kept quiet as the other two stared at her with a mixtures of curiosity and disbelief.

'What happened?' Lucasta asked, quivering with inquisitive interest. 'Did he catch him making a pass at you, or what?'

'Certainly not!' Marion said indignantly.

Gaston gave Lucasta a little shake. 'Of course not,' he said. 'You must not question Marion any more. How would she know why your uncle does anything?'

'Do you?' Lucasta insisted.

Marion shook her head, crossing her fingers surreptitiously. It wasn't quite a lie because she didn't know why he had done it, nor was she absolutely certain that he had. It was just possible that Jean-Pierre had decided to go without any help from anyone.

'I don't believe it!' Lucasta exclaimed. 'I saw Gregory watching you at lunchtime yesterday and he didn't look at all pleased—'

'He often looks disapproving,' Marion said. 'He can't help it.'

'Well, I still think something's going on! Was Jean-Pierre making a nuisance of himself?'

'Lucasta, that is not a proper question,' Gaston rebuked her.

'Marion doesn't mind, do you? It must have been been that! Gregory never interferes with anyone but, if he thought Marion was having a raw deal, he might easily come the perfect host and do something about it. Why should he bother otherwise?'

There was no other reason. Marion admitted it, forcing herself to meet the truth head-on. Illusions could only hurt her more in the end.

Then Gaston laughed, and the illusions came rushing back to mock her. 'I too have seen the way Mr Randall looks at our little Marion,' he teased her. 'He wished to remove the opposition, no?'

'No,' Marion sighed. 'He says himself he doesn't like me.' And, when Gaston went on laughing, she wondered what could possibly be so funny about that. She might have summoned up her courage and asked him, but she was afraid of the answer. There were some things it was much better not to know.

Gaston's car was a huge American Dodge. The cavernous boot swallowed up their few bits of luggage and Marion, with the whole of the back seat to herself, could have lain down full length with the greatest of ease. She wouldn't even have had to cheat by bending her knees.

'Did you buy it here?' she marvelled.

'I bought it from a fellow on the site. He brought it over from the States with him. It's just the job for getting about on these long, straight roads, but no good for your English lanes.' He nodded wisely. 'When I was in an English school in Kent I learned all about your narrow roads. We fell in a ditch and it took us the rest of the night to get ourselves out. Me, I thought we would be sent back to France, but my landlady never told the school I had been out all night. She told me she liked to be known as a brick—Why do you laugh?' he asked Lucasta, offended.

'I love you,' she said.

'You must learn to say it in French,' he encouraged her. '*Je t'aime*—'

Marion stopped listening to them, realising incredulously that they had forgotten all about her. She turned her attention to the road, wishing that Gregory were there to tell her about the desert. Nothing was quite as interesting when he wasn't there, but she wouldn't let it matter to her. She had managed quite well without him before he had gatecrashed her evening class, and she would manage perfectly well without him in the

111

future.

They followed the same road as the one to Madaba until it divided into the ancient King's Highway, the way the caravans of old had taken, and the modern Desert Highway that now meant one could drive all the the way from Amman to Aqaba in a matter of a few hours.

'We must go the short way,' Gaston told them. 'If we went the old way it would be dark before we arrived at Petra.'

The two girls were quite content to leave all such decisions to him. Lucasta didn't mind where she was going as long as she was with him, and Marion was happy that her childhood's dream was coming true and she was on her way to Petra.

It was hard to tell exactly where the desert began. There were odd patches of agriculture beside the road quite a long way south of Amman and, even after the soil had become too barren to support any crops, there were still clumps of green to be seen, as surprising to Marion as were the modern, straight-lined Government-sponsored villages that had been built in the middle of nowhere. The box-like houses had an unfinished look as the metal cords that strengthened the concrete pillars had been left sticking out at the top of most of the dwellings. Some of the buildings were painted and some were not. A strident greeny-blue was a favourite colour, and it did look better under a hot sun than it would have done in the cooler clime of Britain. Colour was obviously more important in the monochrome world of the Moab desert.

Gaston turned his head, still keeping his eyes on the road ahead of him. 'We are turning off for you to see one of the old Crusader castles,' he told Marion. 'Mr Randall said you wished to see one.'

'He's writing a book about the times of the Crusades,' she answered, as if that explained her interest in itself.

'This one was captured by Saladin.'

'How?' Lucasta asked. 'It must have taken a lot of courage to besiege a castle sitting up on an impregnable hill.'

'He bombed it with large stones and it fell down,' Gaston grinned at her. 'He bombed it with giant-sized catapults.'

When they came to the castle, they could see that the Saracen leader had made a good job of destroying the fortress. The castle had been built high above a small oasis where people still lived and farmed their little plots of land. The walls were crumbled rubble and few of the rooms had a roof over them.

Gaston drove right up to it and hastened his passengers out to walk round what was left of the Christian fortress. It was hard work climbing up to the battlements, but the view from the top was more than worth it. After the Saracens had taken the castle, they must have used it themselves for a while, for there were traces of the church having been transformed into a mosque with a *mihrab*, the niche in the wall that points out the direction of Mecca, hollowed out of the already insecure stones.

Lucasta sat on a handy rock and supported her chin in her hand.

'Tired?' Marion asked her.

She shook her head, patting another flat-topped rock beside her. 'No, I was thinking, that's all. To tell you the truth I was wishing Gregory had come with us instead of going to Beirut. Denise looked like the cat who's swallowed the cream, and he—well, he looked kind of sad. I wish he was here with us!'

Marion sat down heavily beside her. Oh my, she thought, but she could say that again! And how! But she was learning the hard way that it didn't do to indulge her dreams.

CHAPTER VIII

They arrived at Petra in time for a late lunch. The road went through the small township of Wadi Moussa, one of the more likely sites where Moses was supposed to have struck the rock with his staff and started a spring of water at which the local people have quenched their thirst ever since.

The Rest House was backed against a cliff, the bedrooms out to one side, grouped above one another and reached by a series of staircases and verandahs.

'I hope they haven't put you too far away,' Lucasta said to Gaston. 'I'm glad I haven't got to have a room on my own.'

'What could possibly happen to you here?' Gaston retorted.

'I don't know—but something might!'

'The trouble with you is that you have too much imagination. It's a good thing Marion doesn't panic easily. You'd both have a terrible night if she did!'

Lucasta made a face at him and watched him load himself up with their luggage without making any move to help him. It was left to Marion to gather up the bits and pieces and to lead the way along the path to the main building. Trees had been planted round the Rest House to make it cooler in summer and the sharp smell of eucalyptus followed them through the swing doors into the reception area and lounge.

A jovial-looking man came slowly across the dim interior and took up his position behind the desk. He checked their passports with infinite care, had them sign their names in the visitors' book, and allotted them their rooms, snapping his fingers for a young man dressed in clothes several sizes too big to take them up to their rooms.

'Your lunch will be ready for you when you come
114

downstairs,' he told them heartily. 'In twenty minutes will be convenient for a very nice lunch!'

To Lucasta's relief, their two rooms had adjoining doors and she had only to knock on the wall for Gaston to knock back. This arrangement suited her very well and she began at once to work out a complicated code that would tell him if she was warm and comfortable, if she needed his help to light the Calor gas that heated the bath-water, or if he was needed urgently because of some as yet unspecified emergency.

'Is this going on all night?' he asked wearily from their open door. 'Marion and I will want to sleep, *chérie*, not play at Morse code!'

'Oh, but, Gaston, I only wanted to make sure that you'd come if we needed you.'

He grinned at her, his annoyance changing to warm affection. 'I shall always come,' he assured her. 'I'll teach you a proper code this afternoon and then you can be sure that I'll understand what it is you are wanting.'

Lucasta's face lit up. 'You know what I'm wanting,' she smiled back at him. 'I'd tell you, only I don't want to shock Marion. I wish—'

Marion stopped taking her nightdress out of her bag and gave the younger girl a meaning look. 'You can go on wishing!' she warned her.

'I know,' Lucasta sighed. 'I'm only seventeen!'

'Sweet seventeen!' Gaston mocked her. 'You cannot say you have never been kissed, *ma mie*. Be content with that and be a good girl. It is not very old, and now that I have found you, I shall not easily let you go.'

'You haven't met my parents,' Lucasta said bitterly.

'There is time for that too,' he comforted her. He looked completely confident that he would come out of any such meeting unscathed. To Lucasta, who had seldom won any of the brushes she had had with her mother in the past, it was a toss-up as to whether she

115

thought him more brave or foolhardy. 'You may change your mind,' he added, his young face tightening at the thought. 'We have to allow for that.'

Lucasta shook her head. 'Gregory says I'm like him in that I never change my mind. I'll wait until I'm eighteen, because you say I must, but I shan't wait a minute longer than that!'

Marion believed her. She rather hoped that Lucasta would not be in her charge when she turned eighteen and achieved her majority. Gregory might dismiss her anxieties about the younger girl as being of no account, but Marion thought she was right to be worried. Lucasta had never had to control her emotions before and she showed few signs of wanting to control them now. Perhaps a few words of warning as to how difficult she was making things for Gaston might be in order, but it was more probable that Lucasta would only be delighted in her new powers over the young Frenchman. She didn't mean to be cruel, but at seventeen she was still very, very young and not entirely responsible.

Marion took her opportunity when she walked down the steps with Gaston, leaving Lucasta to put the finishing touches to her appearance.

'Nobody has ever said no to her,' she told him. 'She was left alone in that house in London with only the servants to look after her. She doesn't realise what she's doing.'

Gaston shrugged his shoulders. 'You see her as a little girl, but she is not that to me. I will look after her, Marion, and see she behaves as she ought, but I think she can look after herself very well. She has always had to look after herself and she has seen much of the bad side of life. Lucasta is nobody's fool. She will be very careful before she finally gives her heart.'

He didn't have to add that he intended that she should give her heart to him. Marion knew that already. She looked at the young man with a new respect, realising that he had summed up his beloved's life far more accurately than she had herself. Lucasta did have the robustness of a young weed, and the native caution of the neglected child who had had to bring herself up as best she could.

'I'm glad she has you,' she said aloud. She smiled at him, glad to lay her burden of care squarely on his shoulders. 'I'm fond of her, disruptive as she can be in any classroom. She's like her uncle in some ways, isn't she?'

She wondered at his amused glance, but ignored it as of being of no importance. It had been a perfectly ordinary thing to say.

'Why didn't you wait for Mr Randall to bring you here?' Gaston asked her.

She was tongue-tied, with a lump in her throat the size of a tennis ball. 'He said he wouldn't. He said nothing would induce him to bring me here!' He hadn't actually said that, but he had certainly implied it.

'He could have told you all about it,' Gaston persevered in the face of her obvious misery.

'They have guides to do that,' she answered.

The restaurant led out of the lounge. It had no windows and was lit by oriental lights hanging from the ceiling, their multi-coloured glass fragmenting the light against the plum-coloured walls. It was only when they were seated at their table that Marion realised they were inside a cave of sorts. The straight walls and ceiling had confused her when she had first looked round the room, but now she could see clearly the marks of the chisels as they had dressed the inside of the soft stone. Had this been one of the dwellings the Nabateans had carved out of the sides of the hills? Was this what she could expect Petra itself to be like?

Lucasta refused to be excited by her discovery. 'Tourist bait,' she scoffed. She put her head on one side, smiling across the table at Marion. 'You're so

117

naïve! ' she decided. 'Isn't she, Gaston? '

' *Elle est charmante*! ' he commented approvingly. but Marion could see that he agreed with Lucasta that she was easily impressed.

' Why shouldn't it be genuine? ' she demanded.

' Maybe it is,' Gaston said. ' The interesting thing is the formation of the roof. Can you see the different colours swirling into one another? It is pretty, no? And it tells much about the rock here. Did you know that Edom means red, that is how the Edomites got their name. Only afterwards did it become Petra, from the Latin word for a rock—'

' Oh, Gaston, don't you start! I don't want to know about rocks and things like that! I want to know about the people who lived here. What do you know about them? ' Lucasta interrupted him.

Gaston grinned at her. ' What should I know but what your uncle told me last night? He said that both the Edomites and the Nabateans claimed direct descent from Ishmael, the first sons of Abraham. He had two daughters, Bashemath and Nabaioth. Bashemath was one of the three wives of Esau, whom sly Jacob tricked out of his inheritance. The Edomites claimed descent from her, and the Nabateans from her sister. They must have been named after her.'

' It was the Nabateans who carved the city of Petra out of the mountainside,' Marion added dreamily. ' I wonder who lived here? '

' To get into Petra you have to go through the Syq. a narrow passage cut by water through the hills. This is outside and vulnerable to attack. Perhaps someone was buried here.'

Lucasta shivered. ' In here? What a horrid thought! '

' Is it not? ' Pleased with her reaction, Gaston forgot his role as an authority on the subject and started telling ghost stories instead until Lucasta was wide-eyed with fright and Marion called a halt.

' Nobody is going to rattle their bones in here,' she

said firmly, ' or anywhere else for that matter. Be quiet, Gaston! '

He smiled gleefully at Lucasta's white face. ' She is a little naïve too, no? ' he said to Marion. ' Drinking in every word of the horrible events of the past. I'm sure she believes that the bloodthirsty Amaziah cast ten thousand Edomites to their death off the top of the mountain! ' He shook his head. ' Not so, not even the Israelites were as cruel as that! The Hebrew word *alaf* can be translated as " thousands ", or " families ", " clans " or " tents "—'

' But some of them were killed? ' Lucasta interposed.

' Of course,' he said. ' The Israelites and the Edomites hated each other. Even after David had claimed sanctuary with them when Saul was trying to end his life, he still sent his general Joab to do battle with them as soon as he came to the throne, and told his army to slaughter them to a man.'

' Who told you that? ' Lucasta breathed.

' Your uncle, who else? ' he laughed at her.

Lucasta smiled faintly, beginning to feel a little better. ' I feel rather sorry for the poor Edomites,' she said.

Gaston chuckled. ' They were good haters, but the Israelites were better! The Hebrews excelled in their Songs of Triumph and loved to dance on the graves of their enemies. When Jerusalem fell to Babylon and poor King Zedekiah of Judah was led away with all his people into captivity, the Edomites, who had had nothing to do with their defeat, sang a triumphant song of their own. " Down with it, down with it, even to the ground," they sang, delighted that Jerusalem, that hated symbol of Judean tyranny, had been reduced to rubble. But the Jews remembered this humiliation over the years. In the 137th Psalm they called on God, " Remember, O Lord, the children of Edom in the day of Jerusalem; how they said, Down with it, down with it, even to the ground "! '

'Did Gregory tell you that too?' Marion asked him, laughing.

Gaston lifted his hands expressively. 'It was not the end of the story. The Edomites moved northwards and became the Idumites and were completely absorbed by their old enemies. King Herod was of their blood, and it was held against him, but he was nevertheless the last of the temporal kings of the Jews.'

'So Edom remained unloved until the end?' Marion said sadly. 'I hope the Nabateans fared better?'

'You will see for yourself,' Gaston promised her. 'Mr Randall says they had the seeds of greatness within them.'

It was a highly satisfactory prospect to be setting out to see some of the flowers that this ancient people had created, Marion thought. She was half in love with them already, if this cave was typical of their achievements.

'What are we going to do this afternoon?' she asked.

'There are horses,' Gaston told her, 'but I have made enquiries and it is better to make one's official visit in the morning, when one comes out of the Syq and there is the Khasneh, the Treasury, the most famous of all the buildings, with the sun on its face. We shall have plenty of time in the morning to do this, and a guide will come with us then and explain it all to us. This afternoon, I thought we might walk through the Syq by ourselves and maybe climb up to the High Place.'

'Marion won't want to do that,' Lucasta decided for her. 'You and I can go up to the top and tell her what it's like afterwards.'

'And what is Marion to do?' Gaston asked her drily.

Lucasta coloured guiltily. 'But you don't want to, do you, Marion? There must be other things to look at!'

'I'll find something,' Marion reassured her. 'If the hidden valley inside the hills stretches for ten square
120

miles, I ought to be able to keep out of your way for an hour or so.'

'You don't mind?'

The younger girl looked so hot and bothered that Marion took pity on her. 'No, I don't mind. I'll have your company for the hike through the Syq, what more can I want?'

Lucasta smiled uncomfortably. 'It's a three-mile walk, there and back,' she pointed out.

Marion broke into delighted laughter. 'I'll try to keep up,' she promised, 'my ancient bones permitting!'

'Oh, Marion, you know I didn't mean that! You're not old at all! But Gaston can't carry both of us, can he?'

'I should hope not!' Marion agreed.

The Syq was the strangest phenomenon she had ever seen. It was rough underfoot, like walking along a dry river-bed which, Marion supposed, was what it really was. The sides towered upwards, perhaps as much as ten times the height of a man, so that only a slit of the sky could be seen if one craned one's neck to look at it. No wonder Petra had been a secret city for so many centuries. If this was the only entrance, the only surprise was that it had been found again at all.

Most of the caves before the entrance of the Syq proper had never been lived in but only used as tombs. Compared to the best examples, they were rough and ready, without the decorated façades that were so much a feature of the main buildings. Only the "Djin" blocks, huge, carved lumps of rock, told of the glories that were to come, and the purpose of these blocks has long ago been forgotten.

When it rained, Gaston told the girls, the Syq could fill with water in a matter of moments. In a flash-flood in the middle sixties, a party of about twenty French people had been drowned there, although they had been told it was dangerous to enter the Syq at that time.

121

Afterwards, a dam had been built to protect the passage, and it was discovered that centuries before the Nabateans had done likewise and had carved a channel right through the mountainside to carry away the water. The same channel is used today.

With the sun shining it was difficult to believe in such disasters. It was exciting enough to press on over the loose stone, trying not to feel completely dwarfed by the massive wall of rock on either side.

Then came the most wonderful moment of all when they came within sight of the Khasneh, or Treasury. It did look pink, a rich salmon pink that was all the more effective after the dim gloom of the Syq itself. The classical façade was breathtakingly dramatic, cut into the rough stone and smoothed to look like the outside of a Roman building. Happily, its position has protected it from the winds that have worn away the embellishments of so much else in Petra, and the bit of the frontage which has come off worst is an urn on top of the monument which was long thought to contain fabulous riches. Many an Arab marksman has tried to shoot it away to release the gold that was reputed to be inside. The practice is now forbidden by law, but eyes filled with longing are still turned upwards. Such stories are hard to kill, and would anyone really want to?

They came out into the sunshine and stood for a moment in the open space in front of the monument. There were no other buildings in sight and it was difficult to judge exactly how big the Khasneh really was. Marion thought she had read somewhere that it was a fraction smaller than the west front of Westminster Abbey, which would make it it about ninety-two feet wide and a hundred and thirty feet to its highest point. Some men sat on the steps, hoping to sell souvenirs from their trays to the tourists who came past, but they paid little attention to the three visitors who had come on foot as they walked into the enormous, gloomy interior.

'Gosh,' said Lucasta, 'how did they do it?'

'In some ways it would be easier than building it up from the ground,' Gaston told her. 'They wouldn't have had to face the problem of putting on a roof.'

'But where did they begin?' Lucasta insisted.

Marion rubbed her fingers against one of the walls and found that the soft red stone came off easily, staining her skin the same red as it was itself. 'They must have started at the top,' she suggested. 'I doubt it would hold scaffolding without falling away.'

'I doubt it too,' Gaston agreed.

They came outside again and one of the men made a half-hearted attempt to show off his wares. Amongst the Bedouin jewellery and foreign coins, amongst them some modern British coins that had probably been dropped by a careless tourist, there was a small clay bottle with a rounded bottom that Marion thought might have been a Roman "tear bottle," in which the Romans are said to have caught their tears before they could fall to the ground. She was sorry that Gaston had refused the man so brusquely, for she would have liked to look at it. When the Romans had taken over Petra they had already been in decline, but she had always thought "tear bottles" to be a romantic conception, and to have one casually offered to her was an opportunity which might never come again.

The main part of the city was further into the valley, cut off from sight of the Syq by the wall of rock into which the Treasury had been cut. But once round the corner it was easy to see the layout of the main part of the city. There were the most famous monuments of the Nabatean Arabs, the Roman theatre, the Streets of Façades, the Roman colonnade street leading to the so-called Kasr el Bint and the museum, and down over to the right to the Christian area of the city, where the Byzantine faith had replaced the pagan gods of old until the caravans of traders had faded away and the citizens of Petra had moved after them, leaving the deserted city behind them to the occasional family of Bedouin who wandered into the Syq and took up residence in the monumental caves for a while. The memory of Petra faded from the rest of the world's memory and it was left in secret isolation until John L. Burckhardt, a young Swiss working for the British Association for Promoting Discovery of the Interior Parts of Africa, of all unlikely institutions, was taken through the Syq by a somewhat irritable and suspicious guide on the excuse that he wished to sacrifice a goat on the very grave of Aaron, the brother of Moses, whom he knew to have been buried within the vicinity.

The steps that led up to the acropolis, the High Place above the valley, were clearly marked, and Marion watched Lucasta with some amusement to see what she would do. But that young lady didn't turn a hair.

'We'll be seeing you, Marion,' she said. 'Don't get lost or anything, will you?'

Marion's eyes sparkled, but she said nothing, merely lifted an eyebrow as the other two began the long climb to the top. She was not entirely sorry to have some time to herself, to drink in the atmosphere of this place which she had always dreamed of visiting. It would be fun to tell Gregory all about it! But would he want to know? The hurt she had felt when he had refused pointblank to bring her hear himself revisited her with a pain that was physical in its intensity. She wondered what he was doing in Beirut, but as that led immediately to Denise and the memory of the gratified possessiveness with which she had pulled Gregory's arm about her, making sure that Marion had seen the gesture, and that was another forbidden subject on this day of days. Marion couldn't help it if Gregory had taken up residence inside her, but she had no intention of allowing him to ruin Petra for her. She would try not to think about him at all and, if the dull ache inside her refused to go away, at least the imaginary ghost of Denise should not be allowed to gloat over her misery. Surely she had more pride than that?

Looking up, Marion saw that the other two were already out of sight. The only sound was of a chicken squawking somewhere in the distance. Away in the distance, a thin plume of blue smoke rose up into the sky, betraying the presence of a Bedouin settlement. Slowly but surely they were being moved out of their tents into solidly built houses, fulfilling their dreams of a more urban existence, with coffee-bars for the men and damp-proof dwellings for the women to gossip away their time to their hearts' content. Their romantic-sounding existence, following their flocks as they grazed the edges of the desert, would come to an end. Their expectations of living more nearly as their neighbours did, already raised by what they had heard on their transistor radios, would finally be realised. When they were gone, Petra would be a ghost city indeed, with only the visit of tourists to bring it alive for a few moments every day.

Marion chose to go up to the Urn Tomb which was not too far away. Some workmen were restoring the crypt below the monument, and she could see them at intervals as she clambered up the steep steps. It was further than she had thought and the ground was rough and a few steps downright difficult to navigate, but at last she reached the top and came out on to a plat-form before the colonnade that guarded the entrance. Inside, she knew immediately that the Tomb had been used for Christian worship by the extra semi-domes that had been carved above where the altar would have been, but nothing could detract from the magnificence of the original building. The swirling pattern of the ceiling, similar to the ringing of an ancient tree, had been blackened by smoke from the Bedouin fires, was even more splendid than that of Al Khan over which the Government Rest House is constructed. Marion sat

125

down on a ledge that jutted out of the wall and allowed her eyes to roam over it, lovingly taking in every detail.

She barely heard the arrival of an American party down below and it wasn't until they trooped into the dim interior of the Urn Tomb itself that she began to listen to what they were saying. Their guide told them that the Tomb was sometimes known as the Royal Courts of Justice, and that it had been thought that the vaulted substructure had been the old dungeons, but they now knew this was not so, for the work now being done had disproved the theory.

The Americans sat in groups, drinking the Coca-Cola that had been brought up for them. The guide himself, carefully dusting his well-polished shoes, sat down on the ledge beside Marion.

'American too?' he asked her.

'British,' she said.

His face lit up and he pointed out through the columns to the flat-topped hill in the distance. 'The British were up there,' he told her. 'Miss Diana Kirkbride was digging there. She borrowed a helicopter from the King to get her equipment up there. Here, she is known as the friend of the Bedouin. She is married now, I think.'

Marion confirmed that she was now Mrs Hans Helback.

'She is a brave woman,' the guide told her earnestly. 'When tourists first came here, they sent the Desert Patrol to guard them, but the local men killed them all. Only everybody liked Miss Kirkbride.' He pronounced it "Kirkerbride". 'Are you married?' he went on with the intimate interest of the Middle Eastern man.

'No,' Marion said. 'Are you?'

He nodded. 'I have three children, but only one wife.'

'But the Koran allows you more?' Marion teased him.

126

He smiled a shy smile. 'But to marry more than one wife you must treat them all exactly the same. That is impossible. Nobody with any sense marries more than one wife nowadays.'

Reflecting on the incident of the lipstick, Marion thought he was probably right. How could you love any two people in exactly the same way?

'I must go down,' she said. 'My friends will be waiting for me.' She searched for the right word to wish him goodbye and triumphantly found it. '*B-khatirkum!*'

He grinned, pleased by the courtesy. '*Ma'-salami!*' He stood up and shook her warmly by the hand. 'You are welcome in Petra,' he added. '*Ahlan was-sahlan.*
'*Ahlan bekum.*'

Marion was smiling to herself as she retraced her steps down to the bottom of the valley. She felt she had acquitted herself rather well. Gregory—But she would not think about Gregory! And why should he care if she had mastered a few basic phrases in Arabic? He didn't care anything about her!

She ran down the last few steps, catching sight of Gaston and Lucasta waiting for her. The horses the Americans had ridden in on were huddled out of the wind and she had to walk round them to get to the others.

'Was it worth the climb?' she asked them.

Lucasta gave her a woeful look, very near to tears. 'No, it wasn't.' Her face crumpled as her control broke. 'I want to go home!'

Marion supposed she must have spent more trying evenings in the past, but off-hand she couldn't think of any. Gaston and Lucasta refused to address more than the most obvious courtesies to each other, maintaining a hurt silence off which her own remarks bounced straight back at her.

'What happened, Lucasta?' Marion asked, when the two girls were getting ready for bed.

'Nothing!' Lucasta insisted, but her woeful face gave her away. 'He was horrible, Marion! He wanted—' Her voice died away into silence and she sniffed pathetically into her handkerchief.

Marion's conscience smote her. 'I should have come with you!' she exclaimed.

Lucasta shook her head. 'He doesn't love me!'

'Of course he does!'

'Not as I love him!'

There was no answer to that. Marion pulled on her nightdress, bracing herself against the cold of the bedclothes. 'I could have done with a hot water bottle,' she said, hoping to change the subject.

Lucasta sniffed again. 'I shan't say goodnight to him. I shan't! He can think what he likes! He'll probably think I'm too young and silly to have remembered his rotten code!'

Marion sighed. 'I should think he can hear every word through the wall if you speak so loudly.'

'Good!' said Lucasta. She heaved herself into bed, pulling the blankets up over her head. 'Goodnight, Marion. It isn't *your* fault!'

But she felt unaccountably guilty all the same. What could have happened up there to upset Lucasta to this extent? Marion tried to read for a while, but wild visions of Gaston trying to force himself on Lucasta kept coming between her and the written word. Common sense told her it was far more likely to have been the other way round, and that worried her too. She should have done something about it, Marion told herself, something more than she had done, but quite what that something should have been she didn't know.

She switched out the light above her bed and fell deeply asleep almost at once. In the night she thought she heard rain pelting down on the roof outside, but dismissed it as being absurd. It hadn't rained once since she had arrived here. At the first light of morning, however, it was still raining. Marion reached over to shake

Lucasta awake, but there was no one there. In an instant she was out of bed and calling her name, but there was nobody there to answer her and, when she felt the girl's bed, it was cold to her touch. Wherever Lucasta was, she had been gone for a long, long time.

CHAPTER IX

They were very patient at the desk. The rain, they murmured, where would anyone have gone in this rain?

' But someone must have seen them! ' Marion interjected. ' Did they have breakfast at any time? '

' I will enquire,' the receptionist soothed her. ' It may be that they have already gone on the horses.' He broke into a flood of Arabic designed to encourage those who were doing their best to mop up the puddles as fast as they appeared on the marble-tiled floor.

' But what am I to do? ' Marion demanded.

The receptionist looked at her with reproachful eyes. ' Are you sure that they are nowhere in the Rest House? ' he asked without much hope. He went to the door and looked out at the teeming rain, his shoulders hunched against his dislike of the wet. Marion went and stood beside him. There was no sign of Gaston's car, but it could have been parked further round the corner out of sight.

' They could have been gone for hours! ' she sighed.

The man beside her quivered like a cat faced with something distasteful, then inspiration struck him. ' You must have your breakfast! You are cold and hungry, no? And afterwards perhaps they will have arrived. I will order your breakfast to be brought to you at once.'

The dining-room, like everywhere else in the Rest House, had been thoroughly disorganised by the rain. The electricity had failed and, as the Cave had no other means of lighting, a Tilley lamp had been lit and placed on a strategic table, accentuating the shadows in the corners and breathing heavily in a way that made Marion hope it was not going to explode. Her experience of oil lamps was strictly limited, confined to the occasional battle with a hurricane lamp, and this one, with its glowing mantle, pump at the ready, and polished exterior, bore little relation to its battered cousin that Marion and her mother kept in the cellar of their house in London "against eventualities", as Mrs Shirley put it.

Toast, jam, and butter were brought almost immediately, together with some hot water with which the waiter invited her to make her own coffee, pointing to the jar of instant powder on the table. In other circumstances, Marion would have enjoyed her breakfast, but her anxieties as to what Lucasta and Gaston were up to had deprived of her any appetite. Yesterday she had felt a thrill to be sitting in one of the actual caves that the Nabateans had carved out of the hillside, today she barely noticed her surroundings. There was no one else in the dining room. The little alcoves round the room were dark and empty, and without the multicoloured glass lights it was hard to see the chisel marks left by the mason who had dressed the stone of the walls.

How could Lucasta have done this to her? Had her quarrel with Gaston been a blind to throw her off the scent of what they had planned together? And, worst of all, *what* was Gregory going to say to her?

Marion was so sunk in misery that she scarcely noticed the tourist policeman as he came in, his Air-Force blue sweater glistening with damp from the rain. He had come right up to her table before she realised he was waiting to speak to her.

'Have you found them?'

His face looked white in the light of the Tilley lamp, without any colour at all, but his eyes were kind and there was no sign that he had any bad news for her after all. She took a deep, gulping breath, and tried to calm herself.

'You have ordered horses this morning,' he said in only slightly accented English. 'They are waiting for you. It is best to have your ride as quickly as possible in this rain.'

131

'But I can't go without the others!' She looked up at his surprised face. 'I must wait for them!' she almost pleaded with him.

'If you wait there may be too much water,' the policeman told her, but Marion wasn't listening.

'Perhaps they went ahead?' she suggested.

The policeman frowned. 'You have some companions with you?' he questioned her. 'A man and a woman?'

Marion nodded eagerly. 'Have you seen them?'

'There are some people who have gone into Petra this morning. I will ask if they are among them. I may not have seen them myself, but they will have signed the book.' He smiled and for the first time Marion saw him as a man and not just at a uniform. It was apparent to her that he had seen her as a woman from the start and she found herself aware of the naked appreciation in his eyes. 'You will come quickly?' he commanded her. 'You will not waste time. The horses and your guide are waiting for you.'

She nodded her head, saying nothing. She wished Gregory were with her. The look in the policeman's eyes had accentuated her vulnerability and she, not normally nervous of being on her own, was strangely reluctant to leave the breakfast table and encounter him again.

It was raining harder than ever when she did go outside. She ran down the path, her head well down, in a mad dash for the tourist office. There was no sign of the policeman there, but the young man who came up to her and shyly introduced himself as her guide seemed to know all about her.

'Have the others gone ahead?' she demanded, rather breathlessly, for her hundred-yard sprint had been faster than she usually travelled.

The young man licked his lips nervously, not liking to admit that he hadn't the remotest idea what she was talking about. He began his introductions all over again.

132

'My name is Fawzi, I am your guide. Please to come this way to the horses.'

'Yes,' said Marion, 'but there should be three of us. The policeman said he would look in the book and tell me if they had signed it earlier.'

The guide swallowed. 'I will look,' he said. He handed her a pen and pointed to the line where she was to sign, watching her closely as she did so. When she had written an impatient flourish that looked hardly anything like her usual signature, he studied the book intently, turning back to the previous page and running his finger down the list of names.

'Well?' Marion asked him.

He closed the book with a bang. 'It may be that they have gone. We must follow quickly.' He smiled beatifically at her. 'There is very much to see and you will want to see it all, yes?'

Marion wondered if she did want to in all this rain. But the thought of what she was going to say to Gaston and Lucasta when she caught up with them drove her on. Indeed, she scarcely noticed the rain as she accompanied Fawzi outside again and down to where the horses were waiting, their heads bowed against the onslaught of the water that was still falling out of the skies. Since she had heard so much about the glories of Arab horses it was rather a comedown to these flinching misshapen animals, strong of back, but with mouths like iron, and amenable only to the soft curses of the men who led them.

Marion eased herself on to the plastic-covered saddle and held on to the toggle that the driver put into her hands. Fawzi, it seemed, preferred to walk, and Marion didn't blame him. She thought she might well have preferred to walk herself, especially when the brute under her poked his way over the rough ground, avoiding the puddles with a delicacy that belied his real nature.

'Fawzi, can you read English?' she asked the young

133

guide just as they were entering the narrow entrance of the Syq, slipping down the slope from the dam.

' A little,' he answered.

Not at all, she thought to herself, and wished she had looked at the book for herself. 'Are you sure they're ahead of us? ' she said out loud.

'Maybe they are.'

In fact, most likely they were not. But it was too late to return. Fawzi would not understand her if she told him to turn back, and the driver's whole attention was concentrated on hurrying his horse along, muttering in Arabic as he did so. Marion recognised the phrase " We are alive, thanks be to God ", again and again, repeated with more and more dislike of the avalanche of water that descended on them.

' *Yellah!* ' Fawzi called over his shoulder. ' *Yellah!* '
' *Yellah!* '

The driver took a firmer hold on the bridle and dragged the horse forward through the stream of water that was already running through the bottom of the Syq. The animal pulled away, stepping round the worst of the puddles and looking for shelter from the sides of the narrow passage so that Marion bumped uncomfortably against the overhanging bulges which she had scarcely noticed the day before when she had been on her feet. With the Rest House scarcely out of sight, she was wet through to the skin and her shoes squelched when she moved them in the stirrups.

The driver looked round, trying to entice the nag into a trot. He caught sight of the anxious misery written plain on Marion's face.

' *Keef halak* ?' he said with a grin.

She knew what that meant. It was something Zein said to her, often and often, and it was she who had lovingly taught her the answer.

' *Mabsut—* ' she began, and only belatedly remembered to put an " a " on the end as she was a woman. ' *Mabsuta el hamdu lillah.* I am well, thanks be to God.'

134

The man nodded. '*Yellah!* Hurry up! ' he roared at the horse.

The channels that the Nabateans had cut into the rock to carry the excess of water away were already full to overflowing. Water streamed down the sides of the narrow passage, splashing into the puddles that grew larger, ran into one another, and began to stream down the slight incline.

'It is a pity you won't see the Treasury building with the sun shining on its face,' Fawzi mourned. His English was better when he was talking about Petra, a subject he knew backwards, parroting his patter with the greatest of ease. 'Have you heard about this building? '

'A little,' Marion replied, nursing her shoulder as her horse crashed her once again against the rocks.

'It is known as the Treasury of Pharaoh. The Bedouin called it that when it had been forgotten why it was built. To the local Bedouin who had no education all sorts of things became the miraculous creations of Pharaoh. He was the evil genius of all their stories, just as Moses was the one who practised only white magic, controlling the natural forces. Had he not brought water out of stone? ' Fawzi looked up at the falling rain and shrugged his shoulders. 'It had to be a magician who had built the Khasneh al Faroun. Faroun means Pharaoh. To men who lived only in tents, it was impossible that men had made such a building. That is why they thought there was treasure in the urn at the top. Pharaoh would naturally hide his gold out of the reach of those who would try to steal it. Nowadays, there is schooling for everyone, and such stories are not believed any more.'

They came out of the Syq at that moment and the salmon-pink facing of the Khasneh dominated their view.

'That is the urn up there,' Fawzi told her. 'This place where we are is called the Wadi al Jarra, the Wadi of the Urn. You know what a wadi is? '

135

'A dry river-bed,' she said.

'It is that, but it is not always dry. Do you want to stop and see inside?'

Marion shook her head. 'I saw it yesterday. I want to find my friends. Could you ask the traders if they have seen them?'

But there were no traders to be seen. Some horses, saddled ready for the non-existent tourists, sheltered under the overhanging cliff beside the Treasury, but their drivers had taken refuge out of the teeming rain and of them there was no sign.

'They will be here,' Fawzi comforted her. 'Or, if they are not, they will be back at the Rest House.'

She wished she shared his certainty. In that instant when she had found Lucasta's bed cold and empty she had known immediately what had happened. She would have been a fool not to know. The pair might have made up their quarrel, or they might never have quarrelled at all, but Lucasta wouldn't have had to wait long before Marion had fallen asleep and then she would have knocked on the wall, using the code they had worked out between them. Perhaps she had even changed her room for Gaston's, laughing to herself because Marion hadn't suspected for a moment what she had been planning. But where had they gone, then? Had Gaston taken her home? Or had he driven her up to look at the site where he was working? It didn't bear thinking about. The Hartley family—and Gregory —had trusted Lucasta to Marion's care, and she had failed them all. She would be sent home to England in disgrace—and what would happen then, with her mother in Devon and determined to sell the house, and herself without a job and absolutely nothing to look forward to?

That Gregory would be furious, she didn't doubt for a moment. It was all right for him to tell her not to worry, but he wouldn't excuse her failure easily. Lucasta was his niece and she was only seventeen.

There were no two ways about it, Marion should have looked after her better!

The tears mingled with the rain on her cheeks and she wiped her eyes on the back of her hand. She was here, in Petra, the fulfilment of a childhood's dream, and she might never go anywhere half as romantic ever again, so she might as well make an attempt to enjoy herself. But the savour had gone out of it. The dream had become a nightmare, black and threatening like the sky overhead. If Gregory were angry with her, the whole of life would be like this, she reflected unhappily. It had been bad enough when he had said he wouldn't bring her here. That had hurt at the time, but the wound he had dealt her was like an aching void within her and it was getting worse all the time.

'You must get off here,' Fawzi broke into her thoughts.

She started, looking wearily around her to get her bearings. Not far away was the Roman theatre, looking bleak and more black than red as the rain ran down the stone seats to the floor of the stage.

'I went up there yesterday,' she said, pointing up on the other side of the Urn Tomb.

Fawzi accepted this with a slight shrug. 'You must visit the Silk Tomb. That is the most colourful of them all. It is like shot silk and beautiful.'

There was nothing to do but dismount. Marion found she had stuck to the wet, cheap plastic of the saddle and, with rather less elegance than she would have liked to display, she slithered down to the ground.

'Come, quickly!' Fawzi urged her.

She wondered why he was in such a hurry, but even as she stood there, the river-bed had started to fill with water and, looking down by the side of the Colonnade Street, she could see it moving relentlessly onwards and, in a matter of seconds, it had turned into a babbling stream that grew deeper and more violent every moment.

137

'There's someone coming,' she said. 'It might be Lucasta and Gaston.'

'We must hurry,' Fawzi said anxiously. 'They will close the Syq and we shall have to stay here if we don't go quickly.'

'You mean we won't be able to get out?'

Such a fate had not previously occurred to Marion, and now that it had, she wondered why they didn't turn round at once and go back to the Rest House.

'We have a little time,' he reassured her. 'I am a good guide and you have given me money to show you a little of Petra. In one day you can't see all of it, you must have two weeks to see everything, but we shall do as much as we can.'

'I want to go back,' Marion objected. 'My friends aren't here, and if they go back to the Rest House they won't know where I am.'

Some young boys clattered past on their donkeys, waving their arms in the air and yelling something to Fawzi as they hurried on.

'We have everything in Petra to be comfortable,' he muttered. 'There is a camp not far from the museum. There is food, everything, and a place to stay.'

'But I don't want to stay here!'

A horse that had followed the donkeys whinneyed gently beside her, and the rider, muffled up to the eyes in his *kaffiyeh*, the cloth some Arab men wear over their heads that is held in place with a black, knotted band, jumped down on to the ground, his boots sending the water splashing up all over Marion's legs.

'You've left it too late to go back now. They've closed the Syq. I was the last person to get through.'

Marion stared at him, unaware of the wet, unaware of anything except his familiar voice. Her heart thundered within her and her mouth dropped open in an astonished delight that would not be denied.

It was Gregory.

138

' But you're at Denise's party! '

' That was last night,' he reminded her. ' Wake up, Marion! This isn't the time or the place for you to go off into one of your day-dreams. I had a hell of a job persuading them that I had to come after you, and I'm in no mood for you to be anything but grateful that I managed to get here! '

But she could only stand there and stare at him, still not believing that it was really he. No wonder he thought her a complete ninny, she thought crossly. If she didn't pull herself together soon, she wouldn't blame him if he lost all patience with her and went away again. And she still had to tell him that Lucasta and Gaston were missing. How was she going to find the words to tell him that? He had *trusted* her—

' Marion, was I wrong after all? Aren't you at all glad to see me? '

' Oh *yes*! '

' Then what are you crying about? '

' I'm not! '

He put his hands on her shoulders and shook her till her teeth rattled. ' Now tell me what it's all about! ' he commanded grimly.

' Oh, Gregory! ' she sobbed. ' How did you get here? Wasn't it a nice party? '

' It had its moments. I drove down through the night, if you want to know. I'd have been here earlier if it hadn't been for the rain.'

Marion sniffed, wiping her face with her hands. ' Didn't you get any sleep at all? ' she asked him.

He shook his head. ' I was looking forward to showing you Petra,' he said wryly.

' But you said you wouldn't bring me here! You said *nothing would induce you* to come here with me! '

He grinned. ' Did I? '

The *kaffiyeh* on his head gave him a rakish air that was borne out by the gleam in his eye. She took a hasty step backwards out of his reach and patted her horse's

139

streaming neck. The animal was remarkably unappreci-
ative, tossing his head and moving away from her until
the driver pulled on the leading rein and took him
away to the nearest shelter. Gregory called after him
and handed over his own mount too, turning to the
young guide and slapping him warmly on the back.

'Well, Fawzi, how are you these days?' he asked
him.

'Well, Mr Gregory, as well as this weather will let
anyone be!'

Gregory chuckled. 'I'm afraid we're stuck here until
it clears up. Will you go ahead to the camp and tell
them we'll want some kind of a meal and that Miss
Shirley will want to try to dry out her clothing? I'm
sure they'll be able to fix up something for her.'

'It is my pleasure,' the young man assured him.

Marion watched him splash his way down the ancient
Roman street beside the line of columns that the
Romans had raised and which an earthquake had
thrown down again, feeling that her last friend in the
world was departing. There was no excuse now for not
telling Gregory about Lucasta.

'Why don't we go with him?' she asked.

He put his head on one side and looked at her, taking
in her agitated, damp features, innocent of any make-
up, her wet clothes that clung to her body in the most
revealing way, and the give-away movements of her
fingers that betrayed her extreme nervousness.

'You're not frightened to be alone with me, are you,
Marion?'

'Of course not!' she denied.

He waited for her smile to break across her face and
was disappointed when it didn't come.

'What's the matter?' he asked her gently. 'I had
hoped you might be pleased to see me!'

If he only knew! Her eyelids fluttered and she hung
her head, searching for some way of telling him about
Lucasta.

'You're going to be terribly angry,' she said abruptly.
'And I don't blame you!' She paused, rallying herself.
'I've lost Lucasta!'

To her indignation he threw back his head and
laughed. 'Is that all? My dear Marion, don't you know
how pleased I am to have you to myself—'

'You don't understand!' she interrupted him. 'It
was all my fault! I should have known how it was, but
I didn't think for a moment they were fooling me. I
thought they'd quarrelled, I really did! But now I'm
not so sure. They must have knocked on the wall and
arranged to go off then—and I *didn't even wake up!* '

'My poor love!' He was still laughing and she cast
him a speaking glance that should have restored his
sobriety but somehow only had the opposite effect. 'I
haven't the faintest idea what you're talking about,' he
went on, still amused, 'and I refuse to discuss it any
further out here in the rain. You can tell me all about
it when we get inside somewhere. Have you seen the
Urn Tomb?'

She nodded. 'Fawzi was going to show me the Silk
Tomb,' she volunteered.

'Then we'll go there. We'll throw in the Corinthian
Tomb for good measure. It isn't the same in the pour-
ing rain, but we'll come again one day and you can
stay as long as you like.'

Her heart turned over within her. When would she
come again? The answer seemed to her to be a certainty. She would never come to Petra again, with or
without Gregory.

She wasn't aware of the exact moment when he had
taken possession of her hand, but when she wriggled
her fingers in his trying to get free, his grip tightened
alarmingly and she gave up the attempt, pretending to
herself that she didn't care either way. But she did.
She liked to feel his strong fingers against hers. She
liked it far too much!

'You should have gone straight to sleep when you

reached the Rest House,' she chided him. 'You must be exhausted!'

He smiled intimately into her eyes and it was like standing in the face of a stiff wind. She couldn't breathe at all and yet it was the most exciting thing that had ever happened to her.

'It felt like crossing the Atlantic, ploughing through all that water,' he said, on the edge of laughter.

She remembered he had talked about America, his new-found-land, before, but she thought he had probably forgotten. Besides, there had been nothing to tell her that *she* was on the right side of the Atlantic. Denise might be there, and she no more than a responsibility, the old country, the one he had to get rid of before he could make his conquest of the new.

Her hand trembled in his. 'Was Denise very angry when you left?'

'She was a little put out. Your friend Jean-Pierre had done nothing to improve her humour by making it very clear that he wished he had stayed behind with you after all.'

'Oh.' Marion was nonplussed by that. 'He isn't my friend.'

'He talked as if he were,' Gregory drawled out.

'Well, he isn't. I don't have friends like that!'

'I'm glad to hear it.'

She peeped up at him, her misery slipping away from her. Did he know, she wondered, that she had to almost run to keep up with him, and, if he did know, did he care?

'I don't see why it should matter to you,' she murmured. 'It was I who had to put up with him.'

He tugged at her hand, hauling her along across the multitude of rivulets that had formed on the rough ground. 'Did you now? Well, let me tell you, young woman, that you'd better forget all about that young man. I now know how the British felt when they disembarked and found the French had got there before

142

them. You were never destined to be French! '

She chuckled, her face bright with laughter. He had been talking about America after all! 'The French had a great reputation for bringing their brand of civilisation to the most remote areas,' she reminded him.

'But it was the British who broke the virgin land to their hand,' he retorted, 'and made it their own.'

Marion missed her footing, recovered herself, and felt obliged to protest at the pace he was setting. 'I can't keep up with you! ' she complained.

He hardly slowed at all. 'Are you trying to? ' he asked her.

'Of course,' she said, 'but my legs aren't as long as yours and you don't make allowances— '

He did slow down then. 'I'll always wait for you, Marion, he said. 'You know that, don't you? Take your own time and set your own pace, I'll be waiting for you.'

'I don't mind running—a little,' she stammered.

'I wasn't only talking about the difference in our strides,' he remarked.

'Weren't you? '

He shook his head very slowly from side to side. 'Will you trust me? '

'I do! ' she exclaimed. She remembered Lucasta and died a little inside. 'Only, when I tell you, you'll never trust me again. You must listen to me, Gregory! Lucasta's gone! '

'Gone where? '

She hunched her shoulders, looking down at her feet. 'She's gone with Gaston. I'm most awfully sorry! I only came here today because I thought they might have come on ahead, and now we can't even get back to look for them. Gregory, what are we going to do? '

His grasp on her wrist tightened, drawing her closer to him. 'What do you want to do? '

'If anything's happened to Lucasta, you'll hate me! '

'Would that be so bad? '

There was no answer to that. His dislike had scorched her to the bone, his hatred would be more than she could bear.

'She could have been gone all night,' she said, trying to bring home to him the enormity of what had happened.

'My dear, there's no need to be so tragic about it. If you hadn't lost your head and gone rushing out into the tempest to look for them, the chamber boy would have given you the note they left for you. They didn't think Petra would be much fun in the rain, so they went off to Kerak to have a look at the Crusader castle there.' His face tightened into sternness. 'I'll have something to say to them for leaving you behind on your own, but I don't suppose they were thinking very straight if they'd quarrelled as you say. Still, it won't hurt Lucasta to learn that other people deserve some consideration from the Hartley clan. She can't learn the lesson any younger.'

Marion ignored most of what he had been saying. 'They left a note?' she breathed.

He pulled her closer still, smiling down at her. 'I'm very grateful to them as a matter of fact, because they also left you to me!' The corners of his mouth kicked up into a distinctly mocking line. 'And I mean to make the most of it!' he added, and kissed her hard on the mouth.

CHAPTER X

His lips were cold and wet against hers. For that first kiss they were no more than tentative, exploring the sweetness of hers with a restraint that confused her. But when she uttered no complaint, the tempo changed and his kisses grew more demanding, leaving her in no doubt as to which of them was in command, and in her heart she was glad that it should be so and she willingly surrendered herself into his arms, straining closer still to the warmth that surrounded her.

'Please, Gregory, don't!' She didn't expect him to pay any attention, but he raised his head and smoothed her dripping hair away from her face with a loving hand.

'Did I pounce again?'

She could feel his laughter rather than hear it, he was holding her so tightly against his ribs. 'No,' she said.

'Well then, why shouldn't I kiss you?'

She had no reason to offer. All she knew was that it was sheer bliss to be in his arms, but that she suspected that it wouldn't last and that away from him the world was going to be a very cold place indeed.

'I'm sorry,' she said.

He tipped up her face to his and kissed her again, very gently and with such tenderness that she ached with her own need for him. 'I'd forgotten that timidity of yours, my little *houri*,' he whispered in her ear. 'But, between the two of us, I don't despair of overcoming your shyness, do you? If I kiss you a little more each day, will you try to get used to my holding you tight and do your best to come to like it?'

Her eyes opened wide. 'It isn't funny, Gregory,' she reproved him. 'You shouldn't have come away from your party!'

He silenced her with his forefinger across her mouth. 'No, it isn't funny,' he agreed. 'You must study your part better than you have done, Marion Shirley. *Houris* are not known for arguing the toss every inch of the way. Their whole existence is to give pleasure and to welcome the attentions of the man who chooses them. Even the most timid ones are not exempt from that!'

'But I'm not a *houri*,' she protested weakly. The whole argument was getting out of hand and she blamed him for it. Why couldn't he accept that she was already aware that the girls he knew would all compete for his favours, and that she would too if she had not known right from the very beginning that she would be badly hurt if she did?

'The picture on your wall gives you the lie,' he mocked her. 'Even Zein could see the likeness between you!'

Yes, and she had not forgotten what he had told Zein when she had remarked on the fact.

'I'm not waiting for you!' she denied.

'No?' His eyes danced with laughter. 'We've already established that I am having to wait for you, and that you don't mind running—a little—to catch up!'

'Gregory, please don't tease me. I know it's only a game to you, but I don't want to play.'

'Why not?'

She wondered what he would say if she told him the stakes were too high for her. But then it was foolish to ask herself that. She knew with a sickening, cold certainty in the pit of her stomach that he would scorn her as a coward.

'I don't gamble,' she said primly.

'I hope you don't!' he replied promptly. He looked down at her for a long moment in silence. 'If this is a game, Marion, I mean to win it. You can dodge the whole celestial army as it marches into Paradise, but you won't escape me, and I think in your heart of hearts you know it.' He smiled suddenly, tapping her

146

cheek to lend force to what he was saying. 'If you're going to bet on anyone, you'd best put your all on me and then you won't lose too much, my love.'

'I'm not betting on anyone!' she declared in a panic. 'I'm not playing!'

'Because you don't want to lose to me?'

She shrugged her shoulders. To lose to him would be a miracle of joy, it was the certainty of losing to Denise that held her back. 'It isn't that,' she said.

She saw the naked triumph in his eyes and gave him a confused look, wondering that it should mean so much to him.

'Then what is it?' he insisted. 'Is it only because you're shy?'

'It's because it wouldn't last,' she tried to explain. 'It wouldn't, would it?'

'That's something you must make up your own mind about.' His voice was very dry, almost as if he didn't care at all. 'But I think I should warn you,' he added, 'that what is mine, I keep, no matter who wants to take it from me.'

His arrogance amused her and her eyes sparkled with sudden laughter. 'Would anyone dare?' she wondered.

His own smile was rather bitter. 'I have never doubted your courage,' he answered.

'Then you should,' she confessed. 'I am often afraid. I'd have been afraid to have been cut off here by myself.' She put her hand back in his with an unselfconsciousness that was very appealing. 'I'm glad you came.'

He threaded his fingers through hers. 'That's reassuring. It's nice to know that you trust me to look after you in such a desperate situation. Thus far and no further, because you still think I may hurt you, don't you?'

She was appalled that he should think her so ungrateful. 'I'd trust you with my life any time,' she assured him lightly.

147

He gave her a quick hug. 'Not yet you don't, my love, but I hope you will one day. You have plenty of time to get to know me better.'

'But I haven't! Whatever you say, I shall have to go back to England with Lucasta. I can't stay with you all by myself!'

But nothing could damp her spirits at that moment. He had left Denise and had come to her and, for the moment, that was enough for her. She intended to enjoy every minute of these unexpected riches and to make it fun for him too. If she possibly could she would make it up to him that he had spent a sleepless night and was now almost as wet as she was.

'So you said,' he remembered. He paused, watching the clouds, heavy with rain, as they drifted through the valley. 'I thought your mother might like to come on a visit and keep you company.'

She was startled out of her moment of contentment. 'My mother? But will she want to leave Devon? I don't think she'll come!'

'She'll come,' he said with certainty.

Marion gave him a frightened look. 'Why do you want to keep me here?' she asked him. She stood in the rain, feeling as though she were about to meet her executioner. His answer meant everything to her. On it turned all her hopes — hopes which he himself had raised only a few minutes before.

'I need you to finish restoring the frescoes. Why else?'

She turned her face away. 'Is that all?'

'What else should there be?' he asked. He was as tense as she, watching her closely as she struggled to hide the despair that swept over her.

'Nothing.' She held her head high and looked him straight in the eye. 'I shouldn't want to lose your castle!'

He shrugged. 'I won't live there for ever, but I shouldn't like to move quite yet,' he agreed.

148

'Where will you go when you leave Jordan?' She was not quite in control of her voice and it trembled lamentably, which she tried to disguise with a cough and very nearly choked. 'To the Lebanon, I suppose,' she said when she could.

He raised his eyebrows. 'Does it matter to you?'

'Of course not!' she denied. But it did matter. It mattered terribly. The Lebanon meant Denise and all that Papa Dain's money could buy. She could see Denise's smirking smile of triumph now and knew she never would have liked the other girl in any circumstances, but that now she was coming perilously close to hating her.

'I like to spend a certain amount of time in England,' Gregory told her. 'Most of the time your mother will have my house to herself, but I always spend at least three months of the year there if I can.'

With Denise? That would indeed make it impossible for Marion to live there no matter how hard her mother tried to persuade her. She would be very alone when she went back to England, she thought, exiled from all she held dear. She didn't know how she would find the strength to endure it.

'My mother will be pleased to see you,' she said formally.

'I hope so,' he returned, and led her firmly forward through the rain.

They had gone some way along the path that led round the western face of El Kubtha when the Silk Tomb came into view. Set well back in a deep excavation as it was, one could see the whole façade at a glance and, even in the rain, it was possible to see the fantastic colouring that had given it its name. Whites, blues, greys, salmon pinks, and plum dark reds, swirled into one another in a brilliant array of natural pigment.

'Oh, I wish I'd seen it yesterday!' Marion exclaimed.

Gregory nodded. 'The colour is everything. Architecturally it isn't very interesting.'

'I don't know enough about it to tell,' Marion admitted.

He pointed out the main features of the various tombs, demonstrating with a stick in the sand the different traditions which had been used and developed by the Nabatean builders. There was the heavy, so-called Crow-step, monumental style that had been imported from Assyria; the Persian influences that had modified the earliest styles; the Nabatean classical façades, heavily influenced by the new ideas from the western civilisation of Greece and Rome; followed by the Byzantine period and the beginnings of decay.

'Didn't the Nabateans have any ideas of their own?' Marion asked when he had finished.

'Their most original genius lay in their irrigation schemes and their pottery. Their pottery is some of the finest the world has ever seen.'

If Marion had not believed him, when they went into the Museum she was able to see a few fragments of their pottery for herself. Most of the best pieces had been taken away to the museum in Jerusalem and, later, to the museum that was being built up in Amman, but there were some fine pieces remaining, impossibly fine and decorated with the leaves of plants in highly sophisticated patterns.

'It's as fine as porcelain!' Marion declared. The quality was all the more dramatic when compared to the much thicker and far less elegant Roman pots that lay alongside the Nabatean plates and bowls.

'It's all the more remarkable when you consider that porcelain is turned out of a mould and these were thrown on a wheel. How did they make such flat and exquisitely thin bowls? Nobody could do it today.'

Marion, who had thrown pots herself during her training to teach, was deeply impressed. 'Are the Nabateans making an appearance in your book?' she asked him.

He laughed. 'No. They had already moved on when my book begins. Most of my characters are land-hungry Normans looking for new estates under the guise of defending their religious sites. They had already moved into England, southern Italy, Sicily, and other places too. Europe was getting too small for them and they burst into the Middle East with enthusiasm. The Crusades were an extraordinary adventure by any standards.'

The museum was in yet another cave, but it was cold in there, and Marion began to shiver, her clothes sticking to her as she dripped all over the concrete floor.

'I think we'd better go over to the camp and get some hot food inside you,' Gregory suggested.

'It's standing about that makes one cold,' Marion said, her teeth chattering. 'I was all right when we were moving.'

But she was glad to follow him down the steps to the floor of the valley and across the Colonnade Street to the camp which had built right into the middle of the ancient, forgotten city. Towels and hot water awaited her and she stripped off her clothes and wrung the worst of the water out of them, hanging them in front of a paraffin heater to dry. She found a blanket and wrapped it round herself as though it were a sarong, fastening it over her shoulder with a large safety-pin from her handbag. When she was ready, she tested her original dress with some anxiety, but, providing she kept reasonably still, she thought it would stay up and she sat down on the edge of the bed and waited for Gregory to come and find her.

It might have been her imagination, but she was sure there was a slackening in the rain when, hugging her blanket to her, she ran across from the tent she had been given to the dining-room beyond.

'What will happen if we have to stay the night?'

she asked Gregory. 'Lucasta will go spare if she comes back and finds me gone!'

He looked amused. 'As you did over her?' he teased her. 'It will do her good to worry about someone else for a change.'

She hoped the rain would abate before then, all the same. If she and Gregory were to be alone there all night what would he expect from her? It was a searing thought; a mixture of ecstatic fantasy and the certainty that she would disappoint him, and it made her more nervous than ever in his presence. How could anyone not be aware of him sitting opposite across the table? She knew every detail of the way he looked with her eyes closed. If she had not known before she would have known now that she was very much in love with him, and she wondered how it could have happened so quickly and with such finality. There would never be another man for her—and that knowledge made her feel lonelier than ever.

'I don't think Mrs Hartley will think I've made a very adequate chaperon,' she volunteered on a sigh. 'Lucasta is sure she's in love with Gaston. I wish I were as certain a match between them will meet with success.'

'But you don't think so?'

She shook her head. 'Gaston won't sell out his independence easily.' She remembered belatedly that it was his sister and brother-in-law she was talking about and said no more.

'I agree with you,' Gregory said. 'But you needn't worry that they'll blame you. It will be something else to be laid at my door.' He grinned. 'My sister has always wanted to run my life for me and she's never been able to understand why her fingers have been burnt every time she tries it.'

An answering smile lit Marion's face. 'Judith?' she prompted him.

'There have been others too. Felicity has a vast

acquaintance all over the world and I have suffered accordingly.'

'I can't see you as an easy martyr,' Marion teased him.

'I try to keep things pleasant — on the surface at least. Blighting unrealistic hopes can be a painful experience, though.'

'I suppose so,' Marion agreed. 'Poor Judith.'

'I wasn't thinking about Judith at that moment,' he responded. 'I was thinking of someone much nearer home.'

Herself? But he couldn't possibly know how she felt about him! Yet there was nobody else that he could mean. The humiliation of the moment swept over her and she tightened her hold on her blanket in an unconscious gesture of defence.

'You might be flattering yourself,' she pointed out in a small voice. 'Or does every girl you meet fall in love with you?'

The glint in his eyes destroyed what remained of her confidence. 'It isn't only love that makes a girl think she might like to marry,' he told her cynically. 'Love is something quite different.' He leaned forward. 'Tell me, Marion Shirley, if I wanted a girl to fall in love with me, do you think she could withstand me for long?'

'I don't know,' she managed to whisper.

'But you must have some opinion on the subject,' he prompted her.

She pulled at her hand, but he wouldn't let her go and she was more afraid than ever that the blanket and she would part company. She gave a final tug to it with her free hand, clutching the edges together as if her life depended on it.

'I don't know anything about it,' she cried out.

'Nothing about love at all?' He leaned nearer still. 'Shall I teach you about love, little Marion?'

She couldn't answer. She simply couldn't! She stared

153

at him, her eyes wide and alarmed. '*No!*' she blurted out.

He sat back, letting go her hand, and managing to look very pleased with himself. 'Perhaps you're right,' he said almost casually. 'This is neither the time nor the place. Are you hungry? Shall we eat?'

She nodded her head, maintaining a dignified silence. But she didn't feel dignified at all. She wished with all her heart that she had had the courage to have said " yes " instead of " no ". Tears blurred her eyes and it no longer seemed to matter whether the blanket stood up or not.

'I'm not very hungry.' She bent her head. If he saw that she was crying, he would despise her, she thought, but the tears kept on coming and her dignity disintegrated into racking sobs that shook her whole body.

Gregory's arms were very gentle as he gathered her up from the chair and drew her down on to his knee. 'Darling, must you?' he asked her.

'I'm not your darling! I'm *nothing* to you!' she wept.

His laughter was very disturbing. 'Having just said you know nothing about it, I shall ignore that remark,' he said, stroking the back of her neck just where the roots of her hair began to grow. 'Marion, if you don't stop it I shall kiss you!'

She gulped back a laugh, remembering how much she had been going to enjoy her day, stolen by the rain for her, with only him to share it with her. 'I'm sorry,' she said. 'I don't know why I'm crying—Gregory! Don't do that! This blanket comes apart very easily!'

'Would that matter?' he mocked her.

'Indeed it would. I haven't a stitch on underneath and I haven't any desire to do a striptease for your benefit.'

'Pity,' he said, his face full of laughter. He set her on her feet and wound her blanket more tightly around her. 'Feeling better?'

His eyelashes were the longest she had ever seen on

a man. How many of his girl-friends had envied him them? She longed to put up a hand and touch his hair where it curled into his neck, but it would never do for him to know how much he disturbed her.

'Thank you,' she said.

His eyebrows shot up. 'For sparing your blushes? I find you beautiful whatever you have on, as you very well know.' He ducked his head and kissed her cheek. 'One day—'

'Mr Gregory! Mr Gregory! The water, it is going down!'

Marion thought he looked far from pleased at the interruption, but it must have been her imagination, for he greeted Fawzi with a genial smile and, putting an arm round his shoulders, drew him out of the door and out of sight of Marion herself.

'How long before we can get out?' he asked.

'Very soon now,' Fawzi's voice replied. 'It is better to go now before you have your food because the rain will start again in an hour or so. The horses are ready to go quickly.'

Gregory glanced down at his watch. 'We'll be ready in ten minutes.'

'I shall be ready too!' Fawzi assured him. 'The lady is all right?'

'She'll do,' Gregory said drily. He turned his head and laughed directly at Marion. 'Pluck to the backbone!' He stood in the doorway until Fawzi had gone and then came back to her. 'Can you brave that horse again, or shall I take you up with me?'

She was shocked by the very idea. 'I'll ride my own horse!'

He came nearer still. 'I'd share more than a horse with you, if you'd let me, Marion Shirley. More even than my frescoes and castle. Will you ever want to share anything with me?'

She hid her face from him, shaking her head. 'I'd want to have exclusive rights,' she said thickly. 'Zein
155

—' She shrugged her shoulders helplessly. 'I wouldn't be happy like that!'

'Are you telling me you're *jealous*?'

She was completely shattered that he should have drawn such a conclusion. And it was the truth. She was torn apart with jealousy, and that seemed less than admirable and she didn't want him to know about it.

'Why should I be jealous? she countered.

'My sweet Marion, I should ask yourself that question. Oh, damnation, why couldn't it have gone on raining for a little longer?'

'Gregory—'

'You'd better get dressed,' he said in quite different tones. 'I told Fawzi we'd be ready to go in ten minutes.'

The moment to approach him had gone, Marion realised, and it might never come again. Once they were back at the Rest House, Lucasta and Gaston would be there, and she saw so little of him at the castle and then there was always someone else there. And at week-ends there was Denise!

It had indeed stopped raining when she went back to the tent where she had left her clothes. There was even the faint glint of gold in the sky as the sun tried to penetrate the heavy curtain of black cloud that hung over the hidden valley. The sooner they were gone the better.

Her clothes were still damp and steaming from the heater. They seemed to have shrunk, they were so difficult to get into and, once she was dressed, they clung to her like a cold compress and were rather more revealing than her blanket had been.

She blushed at the appreciative gleam in Gregory's eyes. 'The worst of it is that I haven't even got a change of clothing at the Rest House. These are definitely tight after the soaking they've received.'

'Mmm,' he agreed, 'they show your figure off to perfection. Very nice too!'

156

Marion looked down at herself, pulling a face. 'There isn't much to show.'

'That's what you think! It's all in the eye of the beholder!'

Was it possible that he thought her beautiful? Oh, she knew she wasn't bad-looking, but compared to someone like Denise she thought she was easily overshadowed. 'I wish I were taller,' she sighed.

He looked amused. 'Do you? I find you enough of a handful as you are! He lifted her and put her on her horse with an ease that left her breathless. 'It isn't too late to change your mind—if you'd rather come with me?'

She found it safer to ignore any such suggestion. What would the Bedouin drivers think if one of their horses had to bear a double burden? Nor could she trust herself with Gregory's arms about her not to want more than he would be prepared to give. Before they had gone a hundred yards she would want his kisses too!

The hooves of the horses clattered over the loose stones, sending the water flying in all directions. Gregory, in better control of his mount, led the way at a brisk trot, turning round every now and again to make sure that Marion was following as closely as possible. There was no hope of her keeping up with him, however. Her driver pulled on the bridle and uttered fierce imprecations, but the horse had his own ideas and chief amongst these was his dislike of getting his feet wet.

'You'd better go ahead,' Gregory said as they were about to enter the Syq. He uttered a sharp command to the driver, who began to run again, tightening his hold on the leading rein. The water gushed through the narrow channel, not now very deep, but fast enough to worry the already agitated animal who clung to the edges, beneath the overhanging sides, bumping Marion badly as he went.

157

'*Ou'a!*' Gregory shouted at the driver. '*Shway, shway!*'

'What did you say?' Marion called back to him.

'I said take care and go a bit slower. He'll have you off if you're not careful!'

But the warning came too late. Now badly frightened, the horse tossed his head, dragging the leading rein from the driver's hand, and made a rush forward, seeking shelter at all costs. Marion could see the bulging rock ahead of her, but there was nothing she could do to avoid it. It hit her on the shoulder, knocking her clean out of the saddle and into the path of Gregory's oncoming mount. She thought that there was no way in which he could avoid her as she staggered to her feet, but even as she was expecting to be ridden down, his hands reached out for her and lifted her clear, holding her tightly in front of him.

It was a long, breathless canter through the pass. Water cascaded down the purple sides, joining the stream that flooded the rough floor. Now and again, the horse beneath them missed his footing, caught himself up with a deep, snorting breath, his nostrils flaring with hatred for this incomprehensible phenomenon, which he had never experienced before and never wished to again.

'I got my way in the end,' Gregory said, laughing. 'Let that be a lesson to you, Marion Shirley. It will do you no good to hold out against me!'

She tried to ease the burden of her weight from the arm that held her, but he refused to give way, tightening his grip so that she could hardly breathe. She was wet and uncomfortable, but it was also a heaven of sorts to be held so closely against him that she could feel the hardness of his body, the ripple of each muscle as he moved in time to the horse's gallop, and the quickening beat of his heart that was only exceeded by the high rate of her own.

When they gained the dam, he slowed his horse's

pace to a trot and then to a walk, allowing her to sit up a little straighter.

'Confess it, Marion, you're not quite as indifferent as you pretend, are you?'

'I don't know what you mean,' she answered. Indifferent! No, she would never be indifferent again, but how could she be sure that he would ever feel the same way?

He gave her a warning tap. 'One of these days I'll shake the truth out of you! Shy you may be, but you'll have to get it together sooner or later, and I mean to be there when you do!'

He swung her down on to her own feet and jumped down beside her, turning his horse over to the waiting Bedouin owner, searching in his pocket for a few coins to pay for his ride.

Marion blinked as the rain began to come down again. Her knees trembled as she tried to walk up the slope towards the Rest House, rushing away from Gregory's potent presence as fast as she could go.

'Marion, where have you *been*?' Lucasta's voice accosted her from the entrance to the reception rooms. 'Whatever made you go anywhere in this rain?'

'I was looking for you,' Marion remembered. It seemed a long time since her panic over the younger girl's disappearance.

'With Gregory?' Lucasta's eyes danced with curiosity. 'Does he fancy you, do you think?'

Marion sniffed, holding her hands tightly together. 'Why do you ask?' she enquired. She stood absolutely still as she did in class when she was afraid that it was getting away from her. 'Does it look like it?'

'Well, no,' Lucasta admitted, disappointed. 'But I was hoping that Denise might have reason to think so. She wants Gregory to get in touch with her *at once*! I don't think she appreciated his walking out on her, and she's waiting for him at the castle. Stand by to watch the fur fly when we get there! Gaston says

159

she's got a very nasty temper, and if he were Gregory, he wouldn't go home at all! She shrugged her shoulders, half in awe and half in admiration for her uncle. 'But it takes an awful lot to face Gregory. If anyone can cope with her, he will!' She put a friendly hand on Marion's arm, gasping as she felt that her sweater was wringing wet. 'Wouldn't it be great if he sent Denise packing once and for all?'

CHAPTER XI

Marion was to remember that drive back to Amman and on to Gregory's castle for as long as she lived. She was surprised to discover that Gregory was not driving the Land Cruiser as he usually did, but a brand new Mercedes that in normal circumstances would have made short work of any distance.

'I'd prefer to travel with Gaston and Lucasta,' she had said as they had sorted themselves out on the parking lot in front of the Rest House. She had gone on to mutter about pressures and, getting more flustered by the minute, that Lucasta was still only seventeen—

'Get in, Marion,' Gregory had ordered her with a touch of grimness that had set her heart working overtime again.

'But I don't want to go in your car!'

His patience had exploded into real anger. 'For heaven's sake get in the car! You'll have to manage without hiding behind Lucasta's skirts sooner or later, and it can't be soon enough for me!'

She had looked at him from beneath her lashes, feeling gauche and insecure. 'I'm only trying to do my job,' she had declared. 'Lucasta is seeing far too much of Gaston, in my opinion.'

'Indeed?' He had opened the front door of the car and had gestured for her to get in, and truth to tell, she had been too frightened not to obey him.

'I'll drip all over the seat!' she had warned him with gloomy satisfaction.

'Too bad,' he had answered. And he had got in beside her without another word, slamming the door behind him, and had driven off without so much as a backward glance to see what the others were doing.

Marion had taken refuge in silence. Half turning her back on him she had stared out of the window at the unrecognisable scenery outside and had given herself up to misery.

It had been Gaston who had told Gregory that Denise had been trying to get in touch with him. 'She sounds—distressed,' he had said delicately. 'She flew down to the Qasr el Biyara to be with you and she was frightened about what had happened to you when she found you were not there.'

It had been impossible to tell what Gregory's reaction to that had been, or so Marion had thought at the time. He had made a telephone call of his own, presumably to reassure Denise that he was on his way home, and had paid their bill at the desk despite her own and Gaston's half-hearted objections. And then he had ordered her into his car with as much ceremony as if she had been a naughty child, and had paid no attention to her since, concentrating on the streaming road ahead of him.

What had Denise said to him? Something to bring him running back to her as though every moment saved on the way was a bonus to be gained with joy.

'You're going too fast,' Marion told him, feeling the wheels slide beneath her.

If looks could kill, she would have fallen down dead on the spot. 'Do you want to drive?' he asked her with commendable calm.

'No, but—'

'Marion, do me a favour and don't say it!'

'The roads are wet,' she finished stubbornly. All right, what if she was stating the obvious? It was her life too he was dicing with if he left the road and crashed the car.

'So are you!' he retorted. 'The sooner I get you back and into some dry clothes the better. Put the heater on and it may warm you up a bit.'

She did so, marvelling at the array of gadgets that the car possessed. 'What have you done with the Land Cruiser?' she asked.

162

'I left it in Beirut. I can travel faster in this one, and I needed to travel fast last night.'

'Oh,' she said.

'Meaning?'

She avoided meeting his eyes by the simple expedient of fiddling with the knobs on the dashboard. 'You must be tired, and I was wondering when you last had a meal. Shouldn't we have stayed at the Rest House for lunch?'

He navigated a tricky piece of road that was completely under water and stepped on the brake once or twice to make sure it had dried out.

'Still not trusting me, Marion?'

The last knob she touched turned on the radio and the car was filled with rhythmic whine of one of the latest Arab pop songs.

'Everyone has to eat,' she said.

'We'll stop for something on the way,' he promised. He took his right hand off the wheel and took hers away from the dashboard, giving it a little squeeze as it trembled in his. 'You don't have to worry. I shan't crash you. Lean back and relax, and try to learn to trust me enough to see you safely home. Okay?'

'Okay,' she agreed. Was she so lacking in trust? she wondered. If so, it was only because he was hurrying back to Denise as fast he could go. If she were loved by him, she would have trusted him with her whole world and everything in it, but she wasn't the kind of girl who allowed herself to rely on someone else's man. She had far too much pride for that!

The desert had taken on the appearance of a swamp. Here and there scrubby tussocks stuck up out of the water, bowing before the strength of the wind and the lashing rain. It was hard to believe that the day before it had been the perfect backdrop for a caravan of camels to pass that way. Now, what animals there were, the black goats and the white sheep, and the occasional herd of camels, looked lost and forlorn, as did the men who looked after them as they sloshed their way along behind their beasts.

Marion wasn't much better off. As the water drained out of her clothes she found she was sitting in a puddle and there was another one at her feet into which her trousers dripped leaving cold trickles down her legs. It would be at least three hours before they reached Amman and another hour after that. Perhaps Gregory had reason to want to cover the distance as quickly as he could.

She was almost asleep when Gregory pulled off the road and came to a stop outside a small café-cum-restaurant. She jerked herself upright and looked about her, surprised by his choice. It looked clean but very little else, and it was raining harder than ever.

'Must we get out here?' she pleaded with him. 'If you're hungry, I don't mind waiting in the car.'

He pushed open the door. 'You'd better get out on this side,' he told her. 'There's nothing but running mud on your side.'

She forced her limbs to move, bracing herself against the wind and the rain. 'I'm cold!' she complained.

'I know you are,' he said with scant sympathy. 'You're probably stiff after coming off your horse too. Will you have tea or coffee?'

She chose to have tea, hoping that it would warm her. It came in a tall glass, without any milk, and she was only just in time to dissuade the man who had brought it from adding several spoonfuls of sugar. It was certainly hot. The first sip she took burned the back of her throat, but she didn't mind at all. She could feel the warmth of it seeping through her and melting the ice that had formed about her heart.

'That's better,' said Gregory. 'You're losing that miserable waif-like look and are beginning to look more like yourself.'

'Am I?' She raised a smile. 'I didn't want to stop, but I'm glad we did. I find I'm quite hungry too.'

164

'Good,' he said.

He left her at the table and wandered into the kitchen area, choosing a tomato here, an onion there, a few eggs for an omelette and a side-dish of ground up chick-peas with olive oil. He came back with several folded crêpes of bread which he put down on the table beside her.

'A new kind of bread for you,' he smiled at her. 'Will you be able to manage without any cutlery?'

'I'm getting quite good at it,' she claimed.

She was. When the food arrived, she tore off a piece of bread and dipped it into the various dishes, taking a little bit of everything. But she was careful to see that he had the major share, for she thought he looked very tired. There were little lines round his eyes that had nothing to do with laughter and which had not been there before. Had Denise cut up rough and, if so, how dared she make him look like that?

'You might have known she'd be angry,' she said at last, watching him sop up the remains of the omelette with his bread. 'I know you were worried about us, and that I was in a state over Lucasta, but we would have sorted it out by ourselves in the end. It wasn't worth making her angry.'

He sat back in his chair, surveying her gravely through his fantastic lashes. 'You've never liked her, have you?'

She blushed. 'That isn't the point! I think she might have waited until you got back, but it isn't any of my business if you allow her to run you ragged. It must be from choice, because you could buy and sell her any time you chose!'

'She has powerful friends,' he excused himself.

'Papa Dain? But you don't need him, surely?'

He looked amused. 'No, I don't need him.'

'Well then?' she prompted him.

'Denise has other friends,' he told her, 'even if you refused the honour. I thought then that it might have

165

been because you were jealous of her. Are you?'

Marion opened her eyes very wide. 'I don't want her money—or her friends,' she asserted.

'My sister Felicity wouldn't be able to do enough for you if you were a friend of the Dains.' The cynical twist to his mouth dismayed Marion almost as much as his words.

'Why should that matter to me?' she demanded.

'Did you know Judith is Denise's cousin?' he murmured. 'Their mothers are sisters, and they all have shares in the family business, under Papa Dain's direction, of course. His is the star to which they've all hitched their wagons!'

'Including you?'

He moved restively. 'I have a certain amount of family feeling. I play along with them. Up to now it hasn't cost me anything to keep the old man sweet. It wasn't likely that anyone would get hurt. My family is not noted for holding their hands when it comes to using other people. Moral outrage is not a feeling that comes their way often, especially not when it comes to their own actions. We haven't got your integrity, little Marion.'

She digested this in silence, testing the truth of what he had told her. She could well believe that the Hartleys were everything he said they were, but Gregory himself? That she could not believe. She thought of the books of his she had read so eagerly in London and she knew why she didn't believe it. His books had a lot of himself in them. She had discovered that bit by bit, living under the same roof with him.

'Does your sister owe the Dains a great deal of money?' she asked finally.

'A great deal,' he concurred. 'The kind of life she and my brother-in-law enjoy is very expensive to support. They are actually his paid employees, but they like to think they are important to him in their own right. They don't like to think he is using them in their turn, yet when he cracks the whip they both jump to it, and when he ignores them for months together the debts mount up and they find themselves bound to him more closely than ever.'

'But he doesn't own you,' Marion stated, knowing it for a fact. 'He never will. Nor will Denise, will she?' She was certain of that. Denise's brand of ruthlessness came in a very pretty package, gift wrapped by her father.

'Are you telling me that you trust me after all?' he drawled. His perceptive eyes were hidden by his lashes, but she had no doubt that they were taking in every change of expression on her mobile face.

'Yes, I trust you,' she said. She schooled herself to sound as though it was a matter of indifference to her whether he sold out to the Dains or not. 'I've read your books,' she added.

'Not very conclusive evidence,' he commented.

Yet she had begun to fall in love with him then, she thought. She hadn't known it; she would have breathed scorn on any such idea; but he had lived in her mind ever since, as much a part of her as the spirit that formed her being.

'I think you know all about moral outrage,' she went on. 'I've never doubted your integrity. I'd trust you anywhere!'

'This is a new departure,' he said wryly. 'I was beginning to think you didn't trust me as far as you could see me.'

She shook her head. 'I wanted to be friends,' she reminded him. 'It was you who didn't want that. You wouldn't be my friend. I knew you didn't like me and I was afraid of—of imposing on you, but that didn't mean I don't trust you.'

'Then you'll trust me to do the right thing in the next few days?' he challenged her.

She nodded. 'Yes,' she said. She didn't doubt that he would do what he thought was right. If he wanted

Denise, he would take her, and she would have to learn to live with the knowledge that he was beyond her reach for ever. Other people had eked out their existence without the man of their choice—and they had survived. And so would she if she had to. What other choice did she have? If it had been anyone else but Denise! She would have to buckle down if Gregory made her his wife, but Marion didn't believe that she would love him as he deserved. There was something essentially hard about Denise Dain.

'And you won't say another word about going back to England?'

She hesitated. 'I may have to go,' she said.

He gave her an intent look. 'I'll keep you here if I have to lock you up to do it,' he said with a fierceness that made her breathless. 'Whoever has to pay for my family's extravagances, it isn't going to be you!'

She stared at him blankly, wishing that she understood him better, but she didn't like to ask the questions that were forming in her mind. Others, less sensitive than herself, would have demanded an explanation without a second thought, but Marion's shyness was apt to tie her tongue in knots, and being in love with Gregory didn't make it any easier for her to gate-crash his privacy.

'Do you want more tea to finish up with?' he asked her.

'I'd rather get home,' she answered.

His face softened dramatically. 'Is the castle home to you, Marion?'

'Sometimes,' she admitted. 'Sometimes I feel I've known it all my life.'

'You know what they say,' he said, though he didn't specify who said it; 'that if you make an image of someone you steal a part of their soul. Your image has been in the castle for many, many years.'

'Will I ever get my soul back?' she wondered. It was only a silly superstition, but the sight of her own face looking back at her from the fresco in her room always disturbed her.

'No, your soul is forfeit to the man who claims you,' he said. 'There are rules about these things, even in Paradise.'

'Perhaps no man will claim me,' she murmured, avoiding his glance. 'What will I do then?'

'Every *houri* is created for some man,' he answered, 'Even the shy ones!'

She managed a laugh, but she was sad inside too. He might flirt with her—a little—but it didn't mean anything to him. It wasn't the sun, the moon, and the stars, as it was to a fool like her.

Moving from the restaurant back to the car was enough to remind her of the damp discomfort of her clothes. She huddled herself into the corner of the seat, thankful that she was no longer actually dripping, and tried to turn the heating up, only to find that it was already to a maximum.

'Are you very tired?' she asked him tentatively. 'I can drive quite well, if you want me to?'

But he refused her offer, smiling as he did so. 'I'll get you home. There will be time enough to sleep then, my dear.'

She wasn't sorry not to take the wheel. The wet roads were dangerously slippery and the Mercedes was a much more powerful car than she was accustomed to driving. When they passed an overturned lorry, there was oil to contend with as well, and she could only admire the way Gregory handled the big car, bringing the slipping wheels firmly back under control with the minimum of effort.

Amman looked unfamiliar in the rain. The steep streets were less crowded than usual, though the horns were as vociferous as ever. The Hussein Mosque, which always looked to Marion as though it had strayed out of a pantomime, it contrasted so sharply with the small, dark shops surrounded it, was closed and locked. Water

169

dripped down the minarets and there were puddles in the courtyard where the faithful normally washed themselves and prepared for prayer. Outside the streets were flooded in places and, in some places, were breaking up under the force of the storm.

'We were lucky to get through the Syq when we did,' Marion mused. 'Do you suppose Lucasta and Gaston are far behind us?'

'Still wishing you were with them?' he asked her.

She shook her head. 'I'll bet Gaston doesn't stop for lunch,' she said. 'I'm getting very greedy, but I do like the food here.'

His grey eyes laughed at her. 'I believe that in spite of the cold and the wet you're enjoying yourself, Marion Shirley!' he accused her.

But then she always did with him.

They arrived at the Qasr el Biyara not much more than an hour later. Marion shook herself out of the pleasant state of lethargy she had fallen into and got stiffly out of the car.

'Run!' Gregory ordered her. 'Run inside and get straight into a hot bath. I'll bring your luggage along later.'

She didn't wait to be told twice. She fled into the castle and went straight down the corridor towards her room. Zein came pattering after her, giggling with the excitement of their sudden arrival. She helped Marion to peel off her wet clothes, running the bath for her and offering to wash her hair for her. When Marion had finally chased her out of the bathroom and had soaked in the hot water for long enough to feel warm again, she chided her in lilting tones for being such a long time and handed her a clean nightdress round the door, followed by a kaftan that doubled as Marion's dressing-gown and something that, at a pinch, she could wear in the evenings as well.

Marion was too tired to argue when Zein set about rubbing her hair dry. She wished they had a language in common so that she could tell her about Petra, but Zein seemed to understand much of what she was saying all the same. 'Mr Gregory,' she said at intervals, and giggled some more. ' *Insh'allah*!' she added piously. 'If God wills it.'

She was setting the final touches to Marion's hair when Lucasta came in and threw herself down on Marion's bed.

'Phew! I didn't think we'd ever get here! But we weren't very far behind you.' She sat up, grinning. 'Have you managed to avoid Denise? You can't hear her down here, but from my room she sounds as mad as a hatter!'

'What about?' Marion asked. As if she didn't know!

'I didn't stop to listen,' Lucasta admitted. 'You see, I wanted to speak to you before I say anything to Gregory. He wants you to stay on here, doesn't he, to finish cleaning his frescoes? Well, you can, because I'm staying too. I'm not going back to school. I'm going to stay here until I'm eighteen and then I'm going to marry Gaston! '

Marion swallowed. 'I see,' she said faintly. 'What will your parents say to that? '

Lucasta shrugged. 'Who cares? It's what Gregory says that matters.' She traced a pattern on her knee with her forefinger and Marion realised she was not as sure of herself as she sounded. 'And what you say,' she added. 'You do like Gaston, don't you? '

'Yes, of course I do,' Marion assured her. ' It's only that you're still very young —'

'And statistically speaking it can be proved again and again that marriages don't work out for teenagers,' Lucasta sighed. ' I know that! But Gaston won't stand for anything else. You may as well know that that was what we quarrelled about. I was sure that if I got him up to the High Place by himself I could make him make love to me, but he wouldn't. He said Gregory would break his neck and quite right

171

too. He says his family is every bit as sticky as Jean-Pierre's, only much nicer, and he expects to find his wife a virgin on his wedding night. So I asked him if he was thinking of marrying me and he said yes, if I still felt the same way about him when I'm eighteen.'

'And supposing you change your mind when you're nineteen?' Marion asked.

Lucasta looked younger and more vulnerable than she had ever seen her. 'I won't,' she said. 'Anyway, there wouldn't be anything I could do about it. They don't have divorces in Gaston's family. He says I'll have to learn to behave myself and go to church on Sundays, and have lots of children like his parents did. Do you know he has *three* sisters and a brother, and they see each other all the time, although two of the girls are married. And I'll see them too!' Her eyes glowed with happiness. 'They'll be my family. Gaston says it's always like that in France. He says he'll have to watch out that they don't spoil me to death whenever his back is turned! Doesn't it sound wonderful?'

'Marvellous!' Marion agreed. She thought that none of them knew how lonely Lucasta must have been in the past. It would be good for her to be part of a large family, but it wasn't a good enough reason for marrying Gaston. She hesitated, not knowing how to put it. 'Supposing Gaston had been an only child —'

'Oh, Marion! We won't always be in France! His work takes him all over the world and then there will only be the two of us. It isn't only his family. You see, I love him very much.'

'Do you?' Marion's face softened. 'It's a wonderful feeling, isn't it?' she said dreamily. 'I'm so glad for you, pet.'

Lucasta, more practical in her approach to the family battle ahead of her, sat up with a bounce. 'You'll probably be the only one who is! And you will help me, won't you?'

'What can I do?' Marion asked her.

'It depends how fond of me you are,' Lucasta began. 'If Denise ever shuts up, Gaston is hoping to have a word with Gregory before going back to the site. If you were to come along too and speak for us, Gregory would be as nice as pie. He wouldn't want to risk putting you out, would he? And he has to be glad that you'll be able to stay on without any trouble to finish his rotten frescoes. I know he meant to send for your mother, but he wasn't half as sure as he pretended he was that she would come. He has dogs and things at his home in Devon and she wouldn't want to leave them, would she?'

Marion really didn't know. It came as a shock to her that even Lucasta seemed to know more about her mother than she did herself. She had never seen her mother surrounded by animals and running a large country house. Her father had been allergic to fur and feathers and a great many other things besides, and her mother had defended him from them all with ruthless efficiency. It was hard to think of her now drooling over one of the enemy.

She sighed, feeling a little sorry for herself. 'I'm not the only person in the world who can clean his frescoes for him! I don't know that I want to stay! I have my career to think about.'

'Rubbish,' said Lucasta. 'Of course you want to stay! I agree Denise is a pain in the neck, but you can always keep out of her way. It's poor Gregory who has to put up with her!'

Marion's mouth tightened into a disapproving line. Poor Gregory indeed! She had never met anyone who was more capable of looking after himself than Gregory Randall.

'Couldn't Gaston speak to him next week-end?' she said out loud. 'He must be terribly tired.'

'Oh, don't be such a mother hen!' Lucasta casti-

173

gated her. 'Gregory is as strong as a horse!'

She eased herself off the bed and cast a critical eye over Marion's appearance, nodding enthusiastically at the waiting Zein. '*Gemil*! Beautiful!' she complimented her. 'You look really nice, Marion. Denise will have to look to her laurels if you're going to wear that kaftan for dinner. It's super!'

Marion fingered the embroidery on the front with diffident fingers. 'It's really my dressing-gown, but it does for way-out occasions too. Do you really think I should wear it?'

'I think it gives you a touch of the exotics,' Lucasta enthused. 'You couldn't wear anything better than that if you want to stir up Gregory. I've seen him looking at you as it is, but in that —! You look a million dollars!'

Marion made no move to change. 'I'm glad you like it,' she said, and tried to ignore the knowing look in Lucasta's eyes, 'but I'm not trying to compete with Denise or anyone else!'

'Not half!' Lucasta retorted.

She hurried Marion out of the room, dragging her firmly down the corridor towards the drawing-room. The sound of Denise's voice came clearly from the room ahead of them.

'It wasn't only me. *Everybody* noticed! Papa was simply furious. If you were going to behave like that, why did you come at all?' She laughed harshly. 'You ought to consider sometimes which side Felicity's bread is buttered. Papa always listens to everything I tell him.'

Gregory's answer was too quiet for them to hear. The two girls exchanged glances and swept into the drawing-room, Marion with her best schoolmistress expression firmly in place.

'Have you dried out yet?' she demanded of Gregory, eyeing his damp clothing with disapproval.

'Not yet.'

'Then you'd better get changed now before we have you in bed with pneumonia,' she snapped, ignoring the light that was dawning in his eyes. Lucasta pulled at her sleeve. 'Oh yes,' she added, 'Gaston wants to see you before he goes, but *not* until you've changed out of those wet things.'

'*Mon dieu*!' Denise exclaimed. 'She is your nanny now too! Tell her to go away, Gregory! We have no need of her!'

'I wouldn't dare,' Gregory drawled, looking Marion up and down with appreciation.

Denise frowned, her eyes narrowing. 'But you dare to displease me! It is too bad of you, Gregory, to be so disagreeable. You ruined the party for me! There was no need for you to be late, and to leave like that was monstrous! None of the other guests could move their cars because you had left the Land Cruiser in the entrance to the drive and nobody could move it. Papa has been indulgent with your eccentricities because he likes you, but he was very angry to find you so inconsiderate.' She gathered herself up for the punch-line, completely sure that she was going to get her own way. 'You will fly back with me now and move the Land Cruiser from the drive! It is the least you can do!'

Gregory opened his mouth to speak, but Marion was before him. 'Fly to Beirut now? I've never heard such nonsense! You can do as you like, Denise, but Gregory is going to bed and *nobody* is going to stop him!'

CHAPTER XII

Denise stood up. She was several inches taller than Marion and she made the most of them, looking down her nose at her as if to make a point of the English girl's insignificance in her scheme of things.

'Papa,' she announced, 'will not be pleased.'

'I imagine he's had worse disappointments,' Marion retorted, standing her ground. 'Besides, if he's such a clever businessman, I'm sure he doesn't allow personal matters to sway his business judgements. It's ridiculous to expect Gregory to go miles just to move a car!'

'You don't know what you're talking about,' Denise told her, affronted. 'It was understood that Gregory and I would announce our engagement at the party yesterday. I had been looking forward to it!' She pouted at Gregory and the tears came running into her eyes.

'Understood by whom?' Gregory enquired, unmoved.

'Papa had heard from Felicity, and if your *sister* doesn't know about your plans to get married at last, who does?'

'You should have tried asking me,' Gregory said mildly.

'Then you do not wish to marry me?'

Gregory shook his head. 'You'd hate it as much as I should, my dear. But if it will make things easier for you, I don't mind telling Papa myself that Felicity was mistaken.'

'If you wish.' Denise shrugged one elegant shoulder. 'What does it matter now? It is Felicity who will have to pay. Papa likes to get his money's worth, and Felicity has made too many mistakes, no?'

Marion bristled with indignation. 'But that's blackmail! she exclaimed.

Denise shrugged again. 'It is the way of the world. If you find the joker in your hand, you must make him count as much as possible. My joker is Papa. Can you produce something better?'

Marion stood very still, squaring her shoulders, her eyebrows slightly raised. 'I don't play cards,' she said. 'Not unless I know the stakes in advance. Did you or your father bother to explain the rules to Felicity by any chance, or are you keeping that particular ace up your sleeve too?'

'What ace?' Denise asked sulkily.

'The one called spite, that's going to put her and her husband out of a job. Or have I misunderstood you? Mind you, I can't help feeling they'd be much better off not to be on your father's payroll, but that's their business.'

'It is certainly none of yours! It is necessary that one of us should marry Gregory and, if I am willing, why should he not be?' Denise made a restless movement, disturbed despite herself by Marion's still dignity. 'I am beautiful, more beautiful than you, so why shouldn't he want me?'

What Marion might have said she never knew, for Lucasta weighed in with a grim determination to defend her parents. 'The Hartleys don't need you!' she declared violently. 'And if you don't know why Gregory should prefer Marion, you jolly well ought to! At least *she* loves him! *She* doesn't weigh him up in terms of hard cash or—or anything like that. She'd be content to live with him in a Bedouin tent if she had to!'

The silence that followed was something tangible in the room. Marion cast Gregory a stricken look and, turning on her heel, rushed out of the room. But Lucasta had not finished yet.

'Why is it so important for you or Judith to marry Gregory anyway?' she enquired.

Gregory gave his niece a wry smile. 'I've been buying up shares in the company. Perhaps I should have told Felicity what I was doing, but she has a managing streak that doesn't invite confidences of that sort.'

'Well, what if you have been buying shares? What does it matter?' Lucasta insisted.

Her uncle made a dismissive gesture with his hand. 'Last year I became the majority shareholder.' His smile grew wider. 'You may not read my books, Lu, but thanks to them I plan to offer Marion something better than a black tent to live in—'

Lucasta gave a little skip of joy. 'And Mother needn't worry, need she? That's good! She'll do anything for you now!. Gregory, will you see Gaston now, and Marion too, because it's frightfully important. Everything depends on your saying yes!' She snuggled into his arm, smiling up at him. 'Marion thinks it's a good idea,' she assured him. 'I've already told her, you see.'

'Baggage!' her uncle said with affection. 'Take Gaston and Marion into my study and I'll be along in a minute.' He gave her a push in the direction of the door and then turned all his attention on to Denise. 'Your father will be wondering where you are. The weather seems to be clearing, but you may have to stay the night if the forecast doesn't get better.'

'I'll drive up with Gaston,' she said stiffly.

Gregory inclined his head. 'As you like. I'll get him to tell you when he's ready to go. Goodbye, Denise.'

But she would not answer. She longed for her father and for him to think of some way she could have her revenge on the man before here. Only this time, she already knew, her father's money would avail her nothing, and that was a shock in itself. All her life there had never been anything she had wanted that had not been bought for her. And she hated Gregory Randall all the more because he had not been for sale.

'How could you?' Marion wept. 'How could you say
178

such a thing, Lucasta? I don't love him—'

'Of course you do,' Lucasta cut her off. 'We all know it, so why pretend about it?'

'Because he might not want me! I *can't*—'

'Of course you can, silly. What are you waiting for? If he's what you want, why don't you tell him so? You may as well get it straight from the start that you'll only marry him if he never looks at the Denises or the Judiths of this world ever again.'

'Lucasta!' Marion wailed, scandalised.

'Not,' Lucasta went on ruthlessly, 'that he liked either of them much, but some of the others have been quite something, and he is madly attractive. You should see them all jostling for position at one of Mother's parties. All he's ever had to do is raise a finger and they've all fallen over themselves to oblige him.' She gave Marion an impertinent grin. 'That's probably why he went to pieces over you! You'd never chase anyone in a million years!'

'Lucasta!' Marion said again, more faintly than before. 'I don't think—'

'Oh, Marion, you're so *square*! Talk about a glimpse of stocking being something shocking! You should see your face! No wonder Gregory talks about candles and good deeds in a naughty world. It just shines out of you. It gives me a kick, so heaven knows what it does for him!'

'Lucasta!' Marion breathed for the third time. 'I *can't* see him again this evening, whatever you say. I have— I have a terrible headache, and he ought to go to bed anyway. He drove all through the night, and you know what the roads were like this afternoon, and—'

'Coward,' said Lucasta with good-natured contempt. 'You no more have a headache than I have. Well, you can play ducks and drakes with your own future, but I'm not going to allow you to muck up mine! Gaston will be here in a minute and you're not going until

179

after he's spoken to Gregory if I have to hold you down in that chair myself! And don't think I can't,' she added, laughing. 'I'm *much* bigger than you are!'

'It isn't fair that he should have to cope with everything now!' Marion blurted out. 'Why can't Gaston speak to him next week?'

'We've been through that before,' Lucasta answered. 'Don't worry so, Marion dear, Gregory can look after himself.'

Even so, the men were a long time joining them. Marion made a pretence of doing her usual round of the ikons, but not even they could soothe her ruffled temper. As soon as she could, she vowed, she would make her escape to her own room and beg Zein to bring her her meal there. By morning Gregory might have forgotten Lucasta's ill-considered remarks and she could avoid him anyway by burying herself in her work, but tonight she simply could not face any more —from anyone!

Gaston came into the study first. He went straight over to Lucasta and took her into his arms.

'It is all arranged, *mon petit chou.* Your uncle is only too pleased to be rid of you as soon as you are eighteen.'

'But, Gaston, I wanted to speak to him myself! I want to marry you as soon as possible, the moment I'm eighteen! I simply can't wait any longer than that!'

'You must do as he tells you, *petite.* He is fond of you, no? And you of him—'

'Nothing will induce me to go back to school!' Lucasta declared, a new fear arising in her mind. 'You did tell him that, didn't you?'

Gaston laughed softly in the back of his throat. 'He told me. He thinks school is not a good place for a grown-up betrothed lady to be and he particularly wishes you to be here with him for the next few weeks. So, all is well?'

180

'Oh *yes*, Gaston! But where is he? I want to see him for myself!'

Gaston laughed again. 'Give the man a chance! He was in the bath when I left him—'

'When he knew we were waiting for him here?' Lucasta said reproachfully. 'I do think men are beastly!' She turned to Marion, apologetic because she had forgotten all about her. 'They arrange everything without us, without the least idea as to whether it will suit us. They could at least consult us, couldn't they?'

Marion stuttered out an answer that meant nothing at all. Happily, it was covered by Gaston's teasing laughter. 'Could you have arranged everything to much better?' he demanded, pretending to box Lucasta's ears. 'I think not! You have a man to look after you now, and that you like very much, isn't it so?'

Lucasta blushed. 'Yes, I do like it,' she admitted. 'There's never been anyone around before. My parents are away more often than not and, although Gregory would always have me in the holidays, I wasn't absolutely certain he always wanted me. But it's different with you. I come first with you, don't I?'

Marion almost prayed that the young Frenchman would say the right thing, now of all times, and she could have kissed him when he did.

'You will always be first and last with me,' he said.

Marion stretched herself and cleared her throat. 'You won't want me here any longer,' she murmured. 'I'm feeling rather tired, actually—'

'Marion, you have to wait for Gregory!' Lucasta rebuked her.

'No, no, he won't want to speak to me now.' She bit her lip and held out her hand to Gaston. 'I hope you have a good trip back to Beirut. We'll see you again next week-end?'

'I'm flying up with Denise,' Gaston told her. 'The weather is clearing, thank goodness, and we should make good time. I'll bring the Land Cruiser down next time I come.' He grinned reflectively. 'That was some scene with Denise, wasn't it? But I think she might have known that there was no hope for her when Mr Randall reclaimed his Mercedes and went rushing off into the night. If I owned a Mercedes like that, it would be like my *doppelganger*, my other self, and I should be very careful of the company it kept!'

'But it's only a car!' Lucasta objected.

'They cost as much as a house does in France,' Gaston told her wryly. 'And that one is custom-built, with all sorts of special features. Mr Randall must be a very rich man to afford that. I wonder if he allowed Denise to drive it.'

'He wouldn't let me,' Marion said in a small voice. 'Goodnight, everybody, I'm going to bed!'

'You can't!' Lucasta cried out.

But Marion was determined. She said goodnight all over again and made a rush towards the door, coming up short against Gregory's large, hard body as he came in. He was dressed in casual clothes that accentuated his tan and he smelt of a mixture of soap and hot water and his after-shave lotion. He put out his hands to cushion the collision and drew her close against his chest.

'You're in a great hurry,' he said.

'I want to go to bed!'

He looked down at his watch and raised his eyebrows. His mouth was not so much disapproving as masterful. 'At this hour? Not even you can choose to go to bed at five o'clock, my ridiculous love.'

If she wanted to, she didn't see why she shouldn't. She made an ineffectual attempt to loose his clasp round her waist. 'Lucasta will want you to herself!' she told him.

'Then Lucasta will have to wait,' he retorted. 'If anyone goes to bed early, it had better be her!'

'Don't be silly!'

182

'Really, Marion,' he reproved her, 'I refuse to be called silly! We have to see our guests off and, even if you are not, I am extremely hungry after all our adventures. And then—' He smiled straight into her eyes, depriving her of all breath. Worse still, he knew it. She could tell by the knowing gleam of amusement in his eyes and the tightening of his hands round her waist. A more formal mode of dress would have been more suitable after all, she thought, for his touch disturbed her badly, sending her heart rocketing off into a new rhythm that he had to be able to feel for himself. 'And then, little Marion, you and I are going to have a talk with nothing and no one to disturb us!'

She stared up at him, unable to wrest her gaze from his. 'They're not my guests—'

He flicked her nose with his fingers, taking a firm grasp of her hand in his. 'I have no other hostess.'

She would have reminded him that he had Lucasta, but he turned away from her, putting her hand with his in his pocket without so much as a by your leave, and threw some car keys across the room to Gaston.

'If there's any trouble speak to Monsieur Dain himself,' he instructed him. 'He has less taste for dramatics than his daughter.'

'I feel sorry for Denise,' Marion put in in a high, clear voice.

'You need not,' he replied. 'Denise has always had several strings to her bow.'

'She was upset,' Marion contradicted him, wondering a little at her obvious attempt to annoy him. Why on earth should she want to make him angry? 'Should she be flying that plane of hers in the circumstances?' She felt Lucasta's look of surprise like a body-blow and blushed. 'I only meant—'

'Shut up, Marion,' Gregory advised her, smiling. 'Denise is the last person to want your sympathy. She doesn't really want to marry me.'

'That's what you say!' she exploded. 'You'll be

183

telling me next that what she really wanted was your Mercedes like—like Gaston seems to think! Well, I don't believe it! Who *wants* a Mercedes?'

His smile grew broader. 'Well, Papa Dain did refuse to buy her one. He said her aeroplane and her Renault would have to do her.'

Was it possible that his Mercedes was as expensive as Gaston had said it was? Marion studied him covertly, noting that while his clothes were casual they were undoubtedly expensive. His collection of ikons too would be way beyond the average man's pocket. Yet nobody ever talked about his money, not as they did about Denise's father, or the Hartleys, or— Her hand trembled in his and he gave it a friendly squeeze. If he were rich, it was even less likely that he would want to marry someone as ordinary and as penniless as herself. Perhaps that was what he wanted to talk about. Perhaps he was going to offer her something quite other than marriage. Marion had always thought of herself as a high-principled person who would never settle for less than a ring and a man's name, but quite suddenly she wasn't sure about herself at all. It was rather a lowering feeling to think that there was very little she wouldn't do if Gregory were to ask it of her. That against him she had no defences at all, and didn't particularly want to build any. It was almost as though she had never known herself at all—any more than she had known her mother would have liked living in the country surrounded by animals and keeping house for a virtual stranger.

'Well, I'd better be off,' Gaston said at last. He hugged Lucasta to him, planting a kiss on her ear and bidding her to behave herself as well as she was able. She snuggled her face against his neck and sighed in despair at the thought of spending a few days without him.

Marion turned her eyes away, a little envious of their unselfconscious expression of their feelings. She tugged at her hand and, winning it free from Gregory's clasp, held it tightly with her other one against her breast. If she made her escape now, she thought, no one would miss her they were all so intent on their own affairs. She tip-toed towards the door and almost had her hand on the door-handle when Gregory scooped her casually back to his side.

'I shouldn't, if I were you,' he warned her.

'But I don't want to see Denise again,' she whispered. 'I'll come back as soon as she's gone.'

'Promise?'

She nodded, crossing her fingers behind her back. Nothing would induce her to leave the sanctuary of her room once she had gained it!

She felt little better than a traitor when he opened the door for her and stood in the doorway watching her as she fled away from him as fast as her feet would take her. It was surely better this way, though, she comforted herself. He and Lucasta would surely find her *de trop* while they discussed plans for Lucasta's wedding and decided how her parents should be told of her forthcoming marriage. They were family, and she—? She wasn't anything in particular to either of them!

She stood in the centre of her bedroom and her eyes went straight to the little painted *houri* on the wall. It was her imagination, of course, but the *houri's* timidity seemed to hide a blaze of happiness that she had never noticed before. Nor was she looking at the approaching troops, not that she ever had, she was looking in the opposite direction, towards the door. How strange that Marion had never noticed that before either.

How long she stood there, rooted to the spot, she didn't know, but she was still there when a slight noise at the door made her turn her head and Gregory walked in.

'Did you knock?' she demanded.

'Did you expect me to?' He came and stood beside

185

her. 'I knew you both would be waiting for me,' he went on in a tone of voice she had never heard before. ' Is it my imagination, or is your image looking distinctly less timid?'

'I thought so too,' she admitted. The funny thing was that she felt less shy herself, considerably so, she was even beginning to feel decidedly pleased with herself. 'I thought it was because I was beginning to get to know her better. I can see the whole fresco from my bed.'

His mouth curved into a smile. 'I know. Before you came I used to sleep in here myself.'

That destroyed her new-found confidence at a blow. 'Did you? But you couldn't see much of her before I cleaned her up.'

'No?'

She swallowed down the doubt that he was teasing her. 'Could you?'

'I liked to know she was there. I talked to her quite a lot, at night just before I went to sleep, and in the morning.'

Marion attempted a small smile. 'Did she answer you back?'

'I was never sure whether she would or not. I had to wait until I met the original girl to find out.'

'Me?'

He nodded gravely. 'You, Miss Marion Shirley. I couldn't believe my eyes when I saw you in that classroom—'

'You shouldn't have been there. You sat there, looking disapproving and making me nervous, and I didn't like you at all!'

'I didn't *like* you either—'

'I knew that!' she declared, tossing her head. 'You weren't at all friendly! As long as I cleaned your frescoes for you, you didn't care at all about *me*! But I have feelings too, you know! It hurt very much that you didn't like me. People usually find me quite

186

tolerable—I don't remember anyone disliking me before! And I tried hard to make you think I wasn't as bad as you thought—'

'I think you're beautiful, darling,' he said, 'but I didn't want you for a friend.' He put his arms round her and drew her close. 'Didn't you ever guess, my little *houri*, that I am in love with you?'

'There was Denise,' she pointed out. 'And Judith. And your sister was very firm about my not being good enough for you!'

He looked amused. 'Did she tell you so? I'm surprised she dared! If she had seen you in action just now with Denise, sailing into action like a pocket battleship, she would have thought twice before she took you on!'

It was very comfortable leaning against his chest and she put her hands over his, holding them closely against her in case he should step away from her.

'You looked so tired,' she murmured. 'When we stopped for lunch, I thought I had never seen anyone look so tired.'

'My trip to Petra hadn't been quite as rewarding as I had hoped,' he said gently. 'You were worried about Lucasta and you weren't thinking of me at all.'

'Did you really come all that way to be with me?' Marion stirred, burying her face in his shoulder. 'I wouldn't let myself believe it in case—in case you had had another reason for coming. You should have told me! All you ever said was that you wouldn't be my friend, and you wouldn't take me to Petra yourself, and I was afraid to let myself hope it might be anything more, that you might have wanted to be with me too.'

'My dear girl, the thought of your face lighting up when you saw me kept me going through every natural disaster that could befall me on that journey. I hadn't anticipated that you would draw the curtains and shut me out in the dark!'

'I've never been more glad to see anyone!' she
187

blurted out. 'I thought you knew and that you were trying to let me down gently. It was a terribly lonely feeling.'

'But now you know better? That you have me at your feet and I love only you? Marion, my darling, how could you think that once I had found my own *houri* to keep me happy throughout eternity, I should want any other?'

'You mean, you didn't know?' She raised her face to his, her eyes wide with wonder. 'Lucasta knew. *Everyone* knew!'

He kissed her very gently on the lips. 'Knew what?' He kissed her again.

'That I love you. I love you very much. I think I always have, only when I saw you that day in London, I didn't know it was you. I got all your books out of the library and it grew inside me as though the seed had always been there, but it was only now growing to its full potential. It's part of me, like the colour of my hair and—'

'Your regrettable lack of inches?' he suggested.

She looked up at him through her eyelashes. 'It has certain advantages,' she said. He raised his eyebrows in mute enquiry, his grey eyes gleaming with laughter. 'I like it when you hold me tight and I can't get free. I liked it very much in Petra.'

'You didn't look as though you did. You looked scared to death.'

She chuckled. 'I daresay you're right and I need practice,' she said, smilingly abandoning herself to the pressure of his hands. 'I'm a very slow learner,' she added, blushing a little at the way he was looking at her. Was she taking too much for granted? 'I wouldn't be scared now,' she added.

'Are you sure?'

She veiled her eyes with her lashes, peeping up at him through them. 'I'm almost sure,' she amended.

If his first kiss was experimental, as though he were

testing the ground, the second one was much less inhibited. Her mouth parted beneath his and she clutched at the collar of his shirt for support as he swept her almost off her feet.

'Marry me, sweetheart?' he murmured against her lips. 'Marry me very soon and we'll share this room and talk to my little *houri* together. Will you be my delightful reward for the rest of our lives? I think you must, because I don't know how I should live without you.'

She pulled back out of his arms, her face flushed with happiness. 'I'd stay anyway, if you wanted me to,' she confessed; 'but if you don't mind very much I'd rather marry you. I'd like the whole world to know I belong to you—'

He smiled and she thought she had never seen him look better or more handsome than he did at that moment.

'Your fate was sealed when I first saw you. There you were, my little *houri* come to life and so much more of everything than the picture I knew so well on the wall. I determined then and there that you were going to be mine, no matter what I had to do to persuade you. We will get married with as much pomp and ceremony as I can contrive, because nothing less will do for me either!'

'*Can* we get married in Jordan—just like that?' she asked.

His hands slid down her shoulders to the small of her back and she trembled beneath his touch. It was only slowly that she realised he was less confident of her than she had supposed, and she thought she would never love him more than at that moment.

'Actually,' he said, 'I thought we might get married in Devon. Your mother is there and can make all the arrangements, which is something she'll want to do for you, don't you think? We could fly back here for our honeymoon. Would you mind very much? Lucasta—'

Marion came back to earth with a bump. 'Where is Lucasta?' she demanded.

Gregory looked embarrassed, but he hid it well. 'She's trying to get a line through to your mother now. She wants to get in first with her offer to be your bridesmaid—once I had persuaded her that we were not going to wait on her and Gaston.' He held her very close and kissed her cheek. 'It will be much quicker in Devon.'

'Then Devon it will be!' she smiled at him. 'Will you show me your house and everything while we're there?'

'It will be your house too,' he reminded her. 'Not that you'll see very much of it for some years to come. Your mother will keep it warm for us, and you'll see her whenever we're in England. It will be home to us all, the children too, when they come along.'

He had had it all worked out from the very beginning. She wondered just how much her mother had known about his plans. It might have been one of the reasons why she had settled so happily in her new surroundings. It gave Marion a new security too, banishing the last of her timidity for ever.

'I love you!' she said. She heaved a great sigh of satisfaction and, reaching up, kissed him on the mouth. 'If I were to live for all time, I'd never be able to prove to you how much.'

But it seemed he had some idea, for his mouth came down on hers again with the masterful touch she liked so much and the flame of ecstasy burned fiercely in them both. In his arms, she had found her paradise.

Have you missed any of these . . .

Harlequin Presents..

All books listed 95c

Harlequin Presents novels are available at your local bookseller, or through the Harlequin Reader Service, M.P.O. Box 707, Niagara Falls, N.Y. 14302; Canadian address: 649 Ontario St., Stratford, Ontario   N5A 6W4.

Have you missed any of these . . .

Harlequin Presents..

All books listed are available at **95c each** at your local bookseller or through the Harlequin Reader Service.